KV-610-196

SWEET & SOUR

ABOUT THE AUTHOR

Dr Rod Settle Th.L, BA, Dip.Soc.Stud., Dip.Ed., Dip.Crim., MA (Criminological studies), Ph.D – has worked for some 35 years in the criminal justice systems of Australia and Papua New Guinea. Within that industry he has handled a variety of roles, including: running an emergency accommodation house for prisoners released from the Victorian prisons system, Stipendiary Probation and Parole Officer in Melbourne, Senior Social Worker concerned with the Children's Courts in Darwin, Associate to the Hon. Mr Justice Raine in the Supreme Court of Papua New Guinea, Education Officer attached to the Advance Training Section of Victoria Police and, latterly, teacher and researcher with the School of Law and Legal Studies at LaTrobe University.

WITHDRAWN FROM UNIVERSITIES AT MEDWAY LIBRARY

MW
KCJS
07000129

3007656

SWEET & SOUR

STORIES FROM THE
WORKING WORLD OF POLICE,
SOCIAL WORKERS, LAWYERS, JUDGES,
GAOLERS AND
OCCASIONAL VILLAINS

Rod Settle

UNIVERSITIES AT MEDWAY LIBRARY
364.
099
4
SETT

The Federation Press
1995

Published in Sydney by:
The Federation Press
PO Box 45, Annandale, NSW, 2038.
3/56-72 John St, Leichhardt, NSW, 2040.
Ph (02) 552 2200. Fax (02) 552 1681.

National Library of Australia
Cataloguing-in-Publication entry

Settle, Rod.
    Sweet and sour : stories from the working world of police, social
    workers, lawyers, judges, gaolers and occasional villains.

    ISBN 1 86287 182 5

    I. Title.

    A823.3

©   The Federation Press

This publication is copyright. Other than for the purposes of and subject to
the conditions prescribed under the Copyright Act, no part of it may in any
form or by any means (electronic, mechanical, microcopying, photocopying,
recording or otherwise) be reproduced, stored in a retrieval system or
transmitted without prior written permission. Enquiries should be addressed
to the publishers.

Typeset by The Federation Press, Leichhardt, NSW.
Printed by Ligare Pty Ltd, Riverwood, NSW

FOREWORD

If you think you've got a glimmering into police culture via various Royal Commissions, or by watching *Janus*, you've got another think coming. What Rod Settle thinks.

Settle's essays on police, policing and social workers in Australia – and on the judicial system both here and in Papua New Guinea – are, I think, wonderful. A shrewd and sceptical observer of the human condition, Rod's work is informed by an uncommon humanity and a considerable compassion.

Rod reminds us that police are the best and worst of people, and that not all aspects of 'police culture' are malign or destructive. You'll find moral indignation leavened with humour and may be affronted, from time to time, by his readiness to be politically incorrect. Nonetheless you'll be impressed by the honesty of the writing as Rod spares neither his subjects nor himself. I like the way he concerns himself with ethical problems whilst remaining tolerant and non-judgmental. Consequently a lot of the best characteristics of the Australian can be found in this unpretentious book.

I vividly remember my first encounter with Rod Settle many years ago. He showed me some pages from a 'work in progress' and, intrigued, I encouraged him to keep writing. A long silence followed. Now, having foolishly followed my advice, he's back. And it was worth waiting for.

PHILLIP ADAMS

CONTENTS

CONTENTS

for my Wantok

In his loneliness and fixedness he yearneth towards the journeying Moon, and the stars that still sojourn, yet still move onward; and every where the blue sky belongs to them, and is their appointed rest, and their native country and their own natural homes, which they enter unannounced, as lords that are certainly expected and yet there is silent joy at their arrival.

S.T. Coleridge,
margin note to the
'Rhime of the Ancient Mariner', 1797

1

FOCUS

Most people working in the criminal justice industry – be they police members, social workers, probation or parole officers, barristers or solicitors, magistrates or judges, gaolers or god-botherers – share some awareness that their occupational role is an odd one. Much of their work is characterised by soul-destroying tedium punctuated by moments of exposure to human tragedy in a stark, face-to-face manner. Without invitation, one becomes enmeshed in the singular secrets of other people's existence which are exposed by the intrusion of the criminal justice system into their lives. The harsh fluorescent lights of the CIB interview room, the focused exposure of the dock of a criminal court or the bald sterility of the 'strip search' area of a prison cell block, both sharpen and degrade the complex humanity of others into grainy, black-and-white footage.

The professionals within this industry – those who manage to maintain their integrity and compassion – must avoid, on the one hand, indulgent wallowing in voyeurism or, on the other hand, the comfortable security of patrician detachment. The professionals are an integral part of that world. Yet it is a world in which their only friends may be their colleagues. Even when officially off-duty they are often treated with some degree of distance by people in 'normal jobs'. Among other things it tends to generate a sense of collective identity which is the experience of some lepers and mercenary soldiers: one of isolation from the genteel jollity of a wider, accepting and cohesive world.

Within the justice machine, one instinctive mode of trying to avoid self-indulgent despair is to develop a soul-armour of dialogue with colleagues. When the patrol shift is over, the court is adjourned, or the cell block is locked down for the night, one tends to seek out one's colleagues of this grim game and share the occasional flashes of humanity which break the bleakness – be they moments of stark tragedy or droll farce – moments of what the Melbourne poet, Collinson, describes as 'being an integer in all this most inelegant, most sad, and O most satisfying business of being human'.[1]

The recounting of such incidents among colleagues is generally permeated by a black humour which is frequently male chauvinistic, often racist and sometimes homophobic, but no offence is intended in the publication of these stories. The brutal humour arises from the black, brutal milieu of the criminal justice industry and I cannot change that milieu. Readers may personally respond to some of the stories with mirth, disgust, delight or distress. As a writer, I can only draw on all the simplicity and integrity which I can muster to relay what I watch and experience.

One of the essential characteristics of such story-telling is the dry but chuckling understatement which allows one to recount human tragedy and still retain that precious kernel of human singularity – dignity and glee. Laconic understatement is its foundation. One of my most respected friends has spent some years as 'a guest of Her Majesty'. Etiquette demands that one never asks an ex-prisoner which crime he was sentenced for but, shortly after I first met Kirky, he mentioned that he had gone down on 'Accidentally discharge a shotgun in a public place'. Spontaneously, and naively, I expressed outrage that he should have served so many years for such a minor offence. 'Well,' he muttered, gazing thoughtfully into his beer, 'I suppose it could have had something to do with the fact that I was aiming it at a bunch of coppers at the time.'

This book is an anthology of stories – some published but most unpublished – written in the course of three decades of work in the criminal justice systems of the State of Victoria and the Northern Territory of Australia and Papua New Guinea in the days when it was a colony of Australia. Some are tragedy, some are farce and some merely explore the 'loneliness and fixedness' of life within the criminal justice machine.

---

1   Laurence Collinson, *The moods of love*, Overland Press, Melbourne, 1957, p. 26.

Most of the chapters below relate to incidents in which I was directly or indirectly involved and which I have abreactively recounted to colleagues. Some chapters (for example Chapters 2, 11, 16, 22, 23 and 26) describe incidents which colleagues have shared with me.

Names and locations have been disguised to protect the not-always-innocent people involved.

HORSE SENSE

The half-lit shop fronts slid silently past. Frost glittered on a passing nature strip. Inside, the car was a warm, softly humming cocoon, its embracing darkness softened by the green/blue glow of the dashboard instruments and punctuated by the unblinking ruby dot above the 'on' switch of the police radio.

> *Camberwell TWO-HUNDRED?*

With reflex action, Macka the constable reached for the microphone. It was getting on to five a.m. and they had been cruising peacefully, oblivious to the chattering radio until their own call sign came up.

VKC, this is Camberwell TWO-HUNDRED.

> *TWO-HUNDRED, what's your current location?*

Brian, the sergeant behind the steering wheel, frowned. 'That means that idiot at headquarters has got a job for someone but has lost track of where all his units are. Damn him, another hour or so and we could be back at the station and making a cup of coffee. It'll probably be a domestic somewhere around here. Give him a bodgie location and he might allocate the job to some other bastard. Tell him we are over on the eastern side of the district – how about, say, Union Road?'

Macka nodded with understanding and squeezed the transmit button on the microphone.

VKC, this is Camberwell TWO-HUNDRED. We're moving north in Union Road.

>*Good, TWO-HUNDRED, have you spotted the horse?*

The what?

>*The horse – HOTEL-OSCAR-ROMEO-SIERRA-ECHO.*

'Aw gawd, he's off his trolley is this bloke', Macka grumbled and squeezed the microphone switch again.

Negative, VKC, we have no visual contact with a . . . er . . . horse.

>*No worries, TWO-HUNDRED, you can't be far from it. We have a complaint of a horse wandering loose in Union Road. Complainant is a Mr Smith – SIERRA-MIKE-INDIA-TANGO-HOTEL. He's a driver with Arrow Cabs – says it's a traffic hazard – he almost collided with it. But don't worry about reporting back to the complainant – you just take the animal into custody: we'll handle the public relations side.*

'Jesus H. Christ!' Brian muttered, exhaling cigarette smoke. 'That's just what we need at the end of a long night shift – a bloody horse! Tell the idiot we'll check it out.'

Macka mumbled a sympathetic obscenity and lifted the microphone.

Roger, VKC, we're conducting surveillance along Union Road.

Brian eased the car into a right-hand turn at the next intersection and headed towards the eastern side of the district. The night shift duty officer would be listening on the same frequency and it was sometimes prudent to be roughly where you said you were.

They drove in silence for some minutes.

'Sarge, I know it's near the end of the shift but it's not such a heavy job. I mean, it shouldn't be hard to find a horse, should it?'

'That's just the problem, mate. If we find it we can hardly put it in the back seat, can we? What do we do? Well I'll tell you mate: *you* get out of the car and hold on to the bloody thing; *I* take the car back to the station, have a cup of coffee, sign off at seven a.m. and go home. With a bit of luck the station may be able to get someone from the municipal pound to take over from you by eight or nine o'clock. Then, if the frost bite is not *too* bad, you should be able to complete all the paper work by about ten and if all goes well you will be off-duty in time for lunch. Have a happy day.'

'Aw, jeez, Sarge, you wouldn't do that to me, would you?'

'Not if I can help it, mate. All we can do is to stall him until the end of the shift. There's got to be *some* job coming up with higher priority than that of a disoriented bloody horse.' They turned up the radio, listening to calls from other units.

Prahran THREE-HUNDRED?

Prahran THREE-HUNDRED.

THREE-HUNDRED, got a domestic for you at Waterloo Street. Are you clear of that last job?

Affirmative, VKC.

Roger, THREE-HUNDRED. It's at TWO-ZERO-FIVE Waterloo Street. Complainant is a Mrs Brown – BRAVO-ROMEO-OSCAR-WHISKEY-NOVEMBER – of that address. Claims she's been assaulted by her husband. That job to you at ZERO-FIVE-TEN.

Roger, VKC.

Macka lunged for the microphone.

VKC, this is Camberwell TWO-HUNDRED.

Camberwell TWO-HUNDRED?

We're close by and can provide back-up for the Prahran van.

> *Roger, Camberwell* TWO-
> *HUNDRED.*

Brian smiled with satisfaction, braked and did a leisurely U-turn in the deserted street. They moved westwards at a gentle pace.

> *VKC, this is Prahran* THREE-
> *HUNDRED.*

> > *Prahran* THREE-HUNDRED?

> *That Code #10 at Waterloo Street*
> *is a noddy. We're at the location.*
> *They're as drunk as skunks and*
> *the husband has fallen asleep. No*
> *great injuries. Civil action*
> *advised. We're resuming patrol*
> *now.*

> > *Roger,* THREE-HUNDRED.
> > *Camberwell* TWO-HUNDRED,
> > *cancel back-up on the last.*

'Aw, Jesus, what do we do now, Sarge?'

'Nothing – hope the bastard at VKC has forgotten us.' They drove in hushed silence.

> > *Camberwell* TWO-HUNDRED?

Macka swore softly.

Camberwell TWO-HUNDRED.

> > TWO-HUNDRED, *what's the*
> > *present situation with your last*
> > *job?*

Well, you see, it was a back-up for
a domestic in Waterloo Street –
WHISKEY-ALPHA-TANGO-ECHO-
ROMEO-LIMA-OSCAR-OSCAR. The
complainant was a Mrs Brown –
BRAVO-ROMEO-OSCAR-WHISKEY-
NOVEMBER – who alleged that her
husband had bashed her. But
Prahran THREE-HUNDRED *–*
THREE-ZERO-ZERO – reported that

*he'd fallen asleep – that's the
husband that is, not Prahran
THREE-HUNDRED – and was
unlikely to hurt her. . .*

*TWO-HUNDRED, I am well aware
of the details of the job given to
Prahran THREE-HUNDRED: **I** was
the operator who gave it out. I had
assumed that you were familiar
with Standard Operating
Procedures which require a unit to
revert to action on the previous job
on receipt of a 'cancel back-up'
call.*

Er . . . which previous job?

*The horse, TWO-HUNDRED, the
horse! You are searching Union
Road for a horse. Confirming that
job to you at ZERO-FIVE-THREE-
ZERO.*

'Poofy little bugger, isn't he?' Macka grumbled, and
squeezed the microphone switch.

Roger, VKC.

Again Brian braked and did a U-turn. They moved
eastward, the car trundling though the deserted streets at a little
over walking pace.

*Any units in the vicinity of
Camberwell Junction? We've got a
minor traffic matter – no injuries.*

Macka snatched the microphone from its hook but his voice
was drowned in a cacophony of three or four units radioing in
simultaneously, each transmission blocking out the others.

*Roger, Hawthorn TWO-HUNDRED.
That job to you at ZERO-FIVE-
FOUR-SEVEN.*

VKC, this is Camberwell TWO-
HUNDRED, *we're quite close and
could handle it.*

> *Camberwell* TWO-HUNDRED,
> *according to my map you're over
> on the eastern boundary of the
> district. Besides, Hawthorn* TWO-
> HUNDRED *is on the way.*

*Er . . . we could provide back-up
for the Hawthorn car?*

> *Camberwell* TWO-HUNDRED,
> *someone handling a minor traffic
> matter is hardly likely to require
> back-up. A milk delivery van has
> clipped the mudguard of a taxi: I
> doubt if the Hawthorn crew are
> going to find themselves
> surrounded by a horde of knife-
> wielding, drug-crazed bikies. In
> any case, you've got a job in
> Union Road.*

Macka replaced the microphone on its hook. 'Fucking little poofs who get these cushy jobs at VKC! Sits on his arse all night drinking coffee and dribbling into a microphone! Wouldn't know which end of a baton to hold!'

Early morning fog drifted through the silent streets. In Union Road the street lights were ghostly orbs haloed by the fog.

It was there that they almost ran into it: it stood stupidly in the middle of the road staring vacantly at their headlights. It was an emaciated draught horse, bones forming angular bumps in a moulting hide.

'Aw Jesus!' Macka whispered desperately.

Brian edged the car forward. The horse blinked, turned slowly and ambled along the street. Brian followed with the car in low gear.

'What do we do now, Sarge?'

'I dunno. Hope the bloody thing falls down a hole or something.' Solemnly the procession threaded its way along the deserted street.

Camberwell TWO-HUNDRED?

Macka swore savagely and lifted the microphone to his lips.

Camberwell TWO-HUNDRED.

TWO-HUNDRED, it is now five past six — ZERO-SIX-ZERO-FIVE. Can we have a situation report on that Union Road job?

Macka clenched his teeth: he had almost exhausted his repertoire of obscene expletives.

VKC, this is Camberwell TWO-HUNDRED. Affirmative, we've found the fucking . . . I mean, we have located the subject of the complaint. We have it under surveillance and are making arrangements to move it into a non-traffic area.

Roger, TWO-HUNDRED, well done! Confirming your reply at ZERO-SIX-ZERO-FIVE.

'And in your ear with a can of beer, you little turd!' snarled Macka without pressing the transmit button on the microphone.

He turned to Brian. 'Sarge, look maybe we could shoo it into a side street where at least no idiot will collide with it. We might even be able to find a dead-end street where we could park the car across the entrance and hold it there while we try to raise someone from the municipal council.'

Brian nodded agreement and eased the car forward to within a metre of the horse's backside.

It stopped and slowly turned a shaggy head towards the two human faces peering through a windscreen. It blinked with large, moronic eyes and sniffed the grill of the stationary car.

Macka unwound the window and awkwardly got his head and shoulders through, his bulbous gut sagging over both sides of the opening. 'Shoo, bugger you, shoo! Move!'

It belched and gazed at him.

Macka extricated his head and shoulders and slumped back against the seat. 'Aw, Jesus, Sarge, it's six-fifteen . . . another half-an-hour and we could be back at the station, making a cup of coffee and finishing off the paper work and getting ready and. . .' His voice trailed off into desolation. 'Anyway,' he added, 'where the hell are we?'

Brian squinted into the fog. 'Union Road . . . I'd say somewhere between Yarrabat Avenue and Belmore Road.'

Macka snapped upright in his seat. '*Where?*'

'I just told you – Union Road, a bit north of Belmore. So what?'

Macka's eyes narrowed and gleamed like a ferret's. Then he bellowed: 'You bloody bewdy! And what's the boundary between Police District "H" and Police District "Y", me old mate?'

Brian paused and a grin began to crease his face.

Macka swung the door open and leapt onto the road. 'Shoo, you moth-eaten lump of uncanned pet food! Over there! Over there!' He waved towards the eastern side of the road.

The horse peered at him and farted.

'Piss off, you brainless bastard . . . go get yourself a job as a VKC operator!' He broke into a disco dance routine, arms waving and hips gyrating.

The horse blinked. It had never before been confronted by an obese dancing constable emerging from the fog and shrieking. It paused, turned and retreated. Macka's dancing and shouting escalated. The horse broke into a shambling trot.

Macka heaved himself back into the car, panting and beaming. Triumphantly he reached for the microphone.

VKC, this is Camberwell TWO-HUNDRED.

TWO-HUNDRED?

Reference that complaint about a wandering horse. It's escaped from

11

*custody: it broke loose in Union
Road and is galloping in an
easterly direction. We tried to
pursue it but we'll be in strife with
our chief superintendent who says
we're not permitted to move into
'Y' District's territory except in
emergencies. But you could inform
Box Hill* TWO-HUNDRED *that they
should be able to pick it up if they
patrol to the east of Union Road
between Yarrabat and Belmore. . .*

3

DEATH OF A BABY

He was ill-suited to the job of senior social worker. Gaunt and clumsy. He had a skinny build with burgeoning beer gut and morose eyes. He interacted awkwardly with the patrol officers, social workers, welfare officers and clerical staff who made up the Darwin office of the Welfare Branch of Northern Territory Administration.

As the senior professional member of the team his duties included supervision and training of the new social workers who arrived regularly from Adelaide, Melbourne and Sydney to spend their first year after graduation working in the Welfare Branch. It was a system akin to that of young interns in the medical profession spending a period in the rough-and-tumble of the casualty department of a public hospital before going into private practice. Most of the fledgling social workers were stylishly dressed young ladies exuding razor-edge sophistication in matters social and adolescent sentimentality in matters professional.

As senior social worker he took his job seriously and genuinely tried to help them through their difficult first year out of university: guiding, supporting, admonishing and being quietly prudent in the allocation of cases to them. His efforts were generally inept. There was Pauline, the dark-haired one, who had arrived two weeks late because her doting mother in Melbourne had turned on a nervous breakdown at the prospect of daughter going to decadent Darwin. For months the mother barraged him with long-distance phone calls, seeking reassurance that her virginal daughter was surviving in the frontier-town world of the Northern Territory; all he could do was to assure her that she was being adequately supervised. The junior social workers were not well paid and, at the end of her twelve month tour of duty, he arranged an escort job for her – the routine task of taking an unwanted baby from Darwin hospital and delivering it to adopting parents in Victoria – so that she could travel home at government expense. He learnt later that the mother fainted when Pauline emerged from the aeroplane clutching a part-Aboriginal new-born infant. So it goes. Sorry about that. But while he could ruefully chuckle about his ineptness in relating to the fears of upper-class mothers, he was conscious that, in the grim work of the Darwin office, there were areas where insensitivity and errors of judgment were unforgivable. The role of the senior social worker in such an outfit is analogous to that of an army lieutenant commanding a combat platoon: the real fighting is done by the troops, and the maintenance of morale and the day-to-day administration is handled by the platoon sergeant; the only significant responsibility of the officer in charge is to have a consistently detached but incisive awareness of what is going on and, in moments of crisis, to make the right decision at the right time. If he lacks the required patience and wisdom, people get hurt and die.

Three new social workers arrived at the beginning of the next monsoon season, when people graduate from the southern universities. He was especially concerned about one of them. Cheryl was a good-hearted kid but had a coy, flirtatious manner which was a mask for a hopelessly idealistic commitment to the social work profession. She insisted on turning up at the office in beads, bangles and tight-fitting jeans and he had to placate the frowning senior clerk.

He allocated a 'child at risk' case to her: a follow-up to a report from Darwin hospital of an infant admitted with severe bruising which, the mother said, had been caused by a fall down some stairs but which looked suspiciously like the aftermath of a bashing. He instructed her to do a low-key home visit and suss out the situation.

She visited the family and, at his insistence, turned in a detailed report of the home circumstances. The report described all the earmarks of a classic 'baby bash' case: a de facto couple in their early twenties, both with memories of physical abuse in childhood, living in the transient, unsupporting atmosphere of a caravan park in the outer suburbs.

Fifteen years in the social work profession had drained him of most humanity and compassion but it had equipped him with a set of warning signals. This case was likely to be a dicey one – a case where a statutory welfare agency could only watch, support and, if it came to the crunch, intervene. He complimented Cheryl on the thoroughness of her report and explained that he would be reallocating the case to an older welfare officer for follow-up.

She protested with a stream of detail about the home visit which showed a good deal of insight. Apparently she had, contrary to his instructions, developed some sort of relationship with the mother, who had at first been hostile but later became eager to unburden herself to 'the lady from the Welfare'. They had talked at length and Cheryl had promised to return.

Fait accompli. Reluctantly, he assigned on-going responsibility for the case to her. It was her first case.

In the second week she reported back to him with details of further home visits. The de facto husband was spasmodically unemployed, had a drinking problem and was not the biological father of the child. He winced. 'Baby bash families' tend to follow a fairly clear-cut pattern and this couple fitted it on all points. He had handled a number of similar cases over the years and was aware that social work intervention was a matter of delicate timing. The last thing needed by such a potentially lethal mixture was the involvement of an eager and naive young social worker. But it was too late: she was already involved.

In the third week she reported some progress. The child responded warmly to her; the mother had come to trust her and seemed to be finding some value in their long interviews. It seemed that the mother was gradually sorting out and articulating her feelings toward the child and to her tenuous relationship with its stepfather.

In the fourth week the child was briefly admitted to hospital with mild burns. The medical report said that it had unwittingly turned on the hot water tap while playing in the bath. Caravan parks in Darwin do not have baths.

At their next case conference Cheryl was agitated. She slumped into a chair in his cluttered office and lit a cigarette. She had, she explained, listened carefully to the mother's prevarications and had reached the conclusion that the baby had in fact been left with the drunken stepfather who, exasperated by its crying, had hurled a mug of near-boiling tea at it. She believed that it was time for the Welfare Branch to step in and take the infant before the Childrens Court as a 'child in need of care and protection'.

He explained the ramifications of such a step: the mental agony of the child torn from the presence of its mother, the emotional starvation of staying in the trim but sterile infants' institution provided by the Administration, the uncertainty of subsequent placements with foster parents. Even if the police laid no charges against the parents, their fragile relationship would certainly disintegrate under the trauma and there would be no possibility of propping them up and getting the child back to them. It is, he explained, the last-ditch decision.

'The situation has reached that point', she said flatly.

He was flustered and fumbled for another cigarette. She spoke strongly and sensibly. The vehemence of her argument seemed to spring from a fairly professional commitment rather than from the sentimentality which he had expected. She pointed out that the social work journals often described closely similar situations which had escalated and resulted in the child's death. Without asking, she reached across the desk and lit a cigarette from his packet. She had, he noted with silent surprise, even studied the local child abuse legislation and was aware that, effectively, the final decision lay with him.

The discussion continued for over an hour: much of it ponderous sifting and re-sifting of the information available and much of it bitchy recriminations about his ability to assess a complex situation. In the end he gave a blunt instruction: there would be no irrevocable intervention but she would monitor the situation carefully with daily visits.

A week later she reported that the stepfather had been on another drunken bender. The child was not hurt but she pleaded for a decision to step in. Again he expounded the consequences of premature action and counselled caution.

On the following weekend he was woken by a phone call at one a.m. She asked him to come to the hospital. He was on twenty-four-hour call-out, with a government car allocated to him, and such calls were not unusual. He stumbled out of bed, gagging on the stale cigarette smoke lingering in his lungs.

She met him in the brittle, fluorescent-lit lobby of the Casualty Department and explained that the child had been admitted on the previous evening with internal bleeding. It had been under surgery for six hours and in the Intensive Care Unit since. Now they had disconnected the life-support equipment and were waiting to finally pronounce clinical death.

She beckoned and he followed her up the stairs to the Intensive Care ward.

They stood on either side of the aluminium cot. The infant lay on its back, flaccid and motionless. She leant over the cot towards him, her face a few inches from his. Her eyes locked on to his and she hissed: 'I just wanted you to see what you've done, you bastard!' She turned and left.

He stood, gazing down into the cot. It occurred to him that he had never actually seen a human being die. His tired mind dredged up a few irrelevant images from films and television. But there were no death-bed speeches, no terminal twitches or resigned sighs. The baby's breathing had long been too shallow to detect and the only thing he could observe was a barely perceptible deepening of the bluishness of the extremities of its fingers and toes.

A young doctor nudged him aside, did a final stethoscope check, and pronounced death.

4

GUSTAVO

Gustavo eventually copped a gaol term in Australia. As a result, I spent a lot of time with him throughout 1992 when he had technically finished his sentence but was being held in custody awaiting deportation.

He was in his early forties, strikingly handsome, with a gentle but commanding presence. He read avidly and spoke English with a breadth of vocabulary which comes from a life-long love of English literature. Physically, he was fit, lithe and clean-shaven. His facial features – especially his eyes – had the symmetry and strength of his Latin American background. He conversed softly but intensely. In his native Bolivia he had worked spasmodically as a small-scale manufacturer of cocaine and occasional drug smuggler. The work had less to do with money-making and more to do with his own hippie lifestyle and personal use of cocaine.

In those days upon days of yarning in the yard of the detention centre, sitting shoulder to shoulder in the shade of the high wall, the conversation would drift between discussions of theology, politics and literature. With the latter, I sometimes felt out of my depth, especially in debates on French existentialist literature as he had read most of the major works in the original French – a bonus from a period in a French prison when one of his import ventures to that country had come unstuck. And, inevitably, the talk often involved the sharing of old personal experiences. Gus is a fundamentally gentle soul with a wry, self-mocking sense of humour who could never bring himself to boasting: instead, he preferred to recount those episodes when he had found himself in incongruous situations and had made a mess of things. Necessarily, we had discussed at length the major debacle which had resulted in his current prison term but, relaxing at the end of long afternoons in the yard, he would often describe with quiet glee some of the minor misadventures of a chequered career. One such absurdity had occurred in Melbourne in the mid-1980s when Gus began practising his profession in Australia.

The cultivation of coca and its processing into cocaine had been a cottage industry in Bolivia for centuries, but all this was to change as Bolivia became sucked into the hegemony of the International Monetary Fund. With the burgeoning demand from the United States for cocaine in the 1970s, the traditional cocaine agriculture of Bolivia was being transformed into a major export industry run by the military government and the police. Bolivia's only other export commodity – tin – was suffering a price slump on the international market. In order to ensure the continuance of foreign aid from the United States, the government felt obliged to produce statistics which gave the illusion that it was actually combating the cocaine trade; typically this took the form of doing occasional round-ups of the petty dealers – individuals trafficking in a few hundred grams at a time – and using them to swell the prison population so that attention was diverted from the major trafficking – measurable in tonnes not grams – which formed the backbone of the nation's economy. Gus was caught up in one such sweep. On release, after twelve months in prison, he found his old carefree way of life less satisfying. Bolivia was changing profoundly. What had once been a loosely organised cottage industry was becoming a massive export trade dominated by oligarchical groups in the police and the military and run on 'Mafia' lines. To keep pace with the competition, and to finance his growing personal use of cocaine, Gus had to become more 'business-like' and concentrate on the hard and increasingly risky work of manufacturing and distributing. This was not the Bolivia which Gus loved: the competition was too hot and the stakes too high and he decided to try Australia. He had befriended an Australian back-packer travelling in South America who had painted a picture of the place as a peaceful one where the Customs Service was inept and one did not always have to compete with the police in drug dealing.

Gus rented a flat in Melbourne, registered himself with the Australian Securities Commission as an 'importer/exporter' and arranged for old friends in Bolivia to forward a crate of Bolivian artefacts – pewter mugs, ceramic bowls and the like – to be sold in Australia. The modus operandi was simple: after taking delivery of the crate one would dump the artefacts in the nearest rubbish bin and carefully dismantle the wooden crate. Several of the slats would be neatly sawed in half longitudinally, grooved out and packed with small plastic sachets of cocaine and then glued back together and sand-papered. The first few consignments came through effortlessly, generating enough profit to forward money back to Bolivia to purchase more cocaine for further shipments to Australia. The project had a self-propelled momentum and had the makings of a thriving business enterprise. Gus had never seen so much money in his life. The fourth consignment was not, however, an unqualified success.

Gus routinely approached the counter at the international freight terminal at Melbourne, exchanged pleasantries with the clerk and signed the delivery docket. Immediately upon doing so, two large, uniformed Customs officers loomed up on each side of him and uttered the words which are the nightmare of any smuggler: 'Excuse me, Sir, but there are some problems with your consignment. Could you step into the office please?'

Gus froze. It was a near-identical replay of the scenario at that French airport years before. Instinctively his eyes darted towards the nearest exit. The door was open but his mind registered that one of the Customs men had a two-way radio attached to his belt: he would alert security guards before Gus made it through the door, let alone sprinted across the lobby and into the car park. Making a run for it was a hopeless prospect. He had checked out the law in Australia and was aware that, with an importation of this size, he would be looking at anything up to fifteen years' imprisonment. He shuddered. Flanked by the two officers he marched slowly and fatalistically into the adjoining office.

As he expected, the room was stark and windowless, containing only one chair behind a large desk. At one end the pewter mugs and ceramic bowls were packed into a plastic container; in the centre of the desk stood the offending wooden crate. One officer stood beside him and the other settled himself into the chair, peering at Gus over the crate. He spoke slowly and deliberately, with that stilted politeness of a bureaucrat. He used his voice with unnecessary loudness as Australians are wont to do when dealing with foreigners, under the misguided notion that it will help them to understand. With the reflex action of someone who has spent some years in prison, Gus snapped to attention before the desk and braced himself for the interrogation.

'Do you speak English?'

'A little', murmured Gus.

'You acknowledge that this consignment is addressed to you?'

They had witnessed him sign the delivery docket and Gus could only nod weakly.

'You do understand, don't you, that Australia is an island?'

Gus's mind whirled, dredging up irrelevant memories of horror stories he had been told of French prisons located on inescapable islands.

'And you understand the severity of the penalties for importing fruit fly?'

Gus tried to conceal his total confusion. Were they suggesting that he was smuggling Spanish Fly? He was an ethical smuggler and would not deal in *that*.

The officer ominously tapped the wooden crate. 'These slats', he said dramatically, *'could* contain fruit fly eggs!' Gus's brain reeled. Was this some peculiarly Australian jargon term for cocaine?

Gus stood there, stunned, as the officer continued. Much of Australia's prosperity, the Customs officer explained, rests on its agriculture; being an island, Australia was blessed with the absence of fruit fly, which ravages so much agricultural produce in other countries; the Customs Service had the task of eternal vigilance to prevent the importation of materials such as untreated timber which might harbour the eggs of the dreaded fruit fly.

Gus's mind steadied and eventually came into focus. He trembled between the imperative of keeping a straight face and that of collapsing into relieved laughter.

'And so, Sir, we are sorry to have caused you inconvenience but you must understand that this is a very serious matter to us. We have carefully repacked the contents of your shipment into a sterile plastic container and we would be grateful if you would now sign this authorisation for us to destroy the empty crate and witness us doing so.'

Gus took a deep breath and solemnly signed the document which they proffered. One officer picked up the crate and Gus followed them to a shed at the back of the freight terminal. He forced himself to stand impassively in the shed, concealing a chaotic impulse to laugh and cry alternately. He had paid $160,000 for the cocaine and that amount would have tripled or quadrupled when it was sold to the dealers, but that was insignificant compared to the prospect of ten or fifteen years in an Australian prison. The two officers methodically fed the crate into an incinerator, totally unaware that they were burning two kilograms of 92 percent pure cocaine.

Gus had, at least for the moment, regained his usual composure. Back in the office he shook hands with each officer and, adopting a passable imitation of someone who speaks little English, congratulated them on their concern for Australian agriculture. He would, he said, ensure that never again would he endanger their lovely country.

Later, outside the terminal building, some passers-by may have been puzzled by the spectacle of a South American gentleman sitting in solitude on one of the park benches, clutching a plastic box of worthless Bolivian crockery and giggling maniacally.

5

MEMBER IN TROUBLE

Gary had been in The Job for almost eighteen months but, oddly enough, had never been directly involved in a 'member in trouble' call. At the recruit academy and at his training station he had, like all the other probationary constables, been taught its mystique: the one signal from VKC which elicited instant response and took priority over everything else. It was a cherished symbol of solidarity among members of an embattled minority group – a call with a mystique which was, perhaps, out of proportion to the number of times it was actually used.

He had his first experience of it on a six p.m. to two a.m. shift on the car with Don, the senior constable, towards the end of winter.

Ostensibly they were allocated to a 'stake out' job: waiting patiently to see if a sexual kink, reported as prowling a particular street at that time of night on several occasions in the past week, would show up again. But the station senior sergeant's organising skills were at their usual level: one of the unmarked cars was in the police garages for repair, the other was being used by the CIB, and they were given the station patrol car. Its prominent blue light, siren and insignia rendered the exercise rather pointless and all they could do was to park, as unobtrusively as possible beneath the shadow of a tree in a nearby side street, in the forlorn hope that someone would phone in a complaint which would be relayed to them by radio.

They doused all lights on the car and settled down to several hours of pointless, silent waiting. After three-quarters-of-an-hour Don fidgeted, grinned and said: 'Oh, the hell with it! Forget what I said about complete darkness and no cigarettes'. They smoked, cupping hands around cigarettes, and chatted softly. The radio was turned down to a quiet drone. Idly they followed in their minds the movements of the couple of dozen other vehicles using this channel.

Gary remembered a civilian who had accompanied them on a shift earlier in the year – some academic doing research on policing – and his amazement at how they could gossip, drive, exchange jokes and banter while being instinctively aware of the flowing pattern of a dozen or so other mobile units – an ever-changing pattern adumbrated by the babbling radio. It is an almost unconscious process. On a long, routine shift you become part of the patrolling car and its garrulous radio which, in turn, is part of a network of similar vehicles on the move, and your mind routinely registers the whereabouts of the others.

Rain began to pad on the car roof. They did not want to switch on the wipers and the windscreen became a glittering sheet of tiny pearls.

They both tacitly noted from the babbling radio that the Preston van was handling a call to a disturbance at a block of flats in Thornbury. That would be Myxo Morris, the senior constable, and Christine, the young policewoman. Gary's mind galloped through a few brief erotic fantasies: Christine was the vibrant kid who often had a cup of coffee with him in the mess room. Even the drab cut of a policewoman's uniform could not deaden the shape of that trim little bum. He tried to picture it naked and moving.

VKC gave the usual request for a unit to back-up the Preston van but Gary and Don did not respond as they were over on the other side of the district, five or six kilometres away, and there were plenty of units in the Thornbury area. They overheard the Northcote van replying and also a Heidelberg crime car unit indicating that they were a couple of kilometres to the north.

The rain increased to a steady patter and they were conscious of the stillness of the car's interior. Don composed his face into mock solemnity and mimicked the Chief Commissioner's voice. 'The modern policeman must not become encapsulated in his vehicle!' he intoned and Gary chuckled. It was an in-group joke: a cliché beloved of the Chief Commissioner who managed to slip it into most of the speeches he made to his men.

With a start, they fell silent simultaneously. The call coming through from the Preston van to 'speed up back-up' was a bit unusual. Presumably Myxo and Christine had reached the location and found it to be a heavier job than expected. They could faintly hear the Heidelberg unit radioing that he was on the move.

Gary and Don, a considerable distance away, could hear VKC's powerful transmitter loud and clear but could follow only snatches of the radio traffic coming back from the small radios of units on the road. Christine's voice came through the jumble of transmissions on the overcrowded channel; apparently Myxo was out of the van, either leaving her to handle the radio or else sending her back to do so. Her soft voice was impossible to understand but they could catch background noise of shouted abuse. There was a confused interchange as a CIB unit radioed in a routine message, blocking out what she was saying, and being curtly told by the VKC operator to 'Stand by!' Her voice continued and, again, there was a turmoil of shouting in the background. The VKC operator patiently and persistently demanded more specific information from her. Eventually he cut across her transmission and gave the magic signal.

He could not have been through the first three syllables of the phrase 'Member in trouble' before Don had the car moving. Turn the ignition key, slam into gear, flick on the light and siren – they happened almost simultaneously.

Gary was pushed back into the seat by the acceleration. He adjusted his seat belt and turned the radio up. They did a savage swing into Rosanna Road with the rear wheels whining on the slippery surface.

As far as they could make out from the overlapping radio messages, the van crew had pulled in beside a bunch of drunken bucks spilling out of the main entrance of the flats; Myxo had stepped out and found himself confronted by about twenty of them. It seemed that there was some breakage of glass and some attempt to overturn the van.

There was no point in Gary advising VKC of their location: they were still a couple of kilometres away and the channel had erupted into a cacophony of calls from closer units.

Don pushed the car to its limits. The rigid, grid-iron lay-out of the streets of Melbourne's northern suburbs meant that they could not move diagonally across the chess board with the smoothness of a bishop: it was the jagged stop/start movement of a knight. And it seemed that every intersection had a red light against them. Don would nudge the car a third of the way across, impatiently checking that all four lanes of traffic had heard the wailing siren, and then slam the car through a violent turn.

At the corner of Dundas Street, Gary closed his eyes and involuntarily tightened his safety belt as Don coped with the incongruous situation of an ambulance hurtling west across the intersection on a different job. Neither could hear the other's siren. Don braked with an abruptness which slewed the rear wheels to the right, slamming Gary's shoulder against the door frame, and then accelerated with a savageness which pushed him back into position.

Gary had been on several high-speed chases with Don but had never seen him drive with such concentrated grimness.

They missed the turn-off into Clarendon Street and floundered among the small streets to the south. They swung into Kemp Street, only to find that there was no way over or under the railway line. Gary, clutching the street directory, shouted directions at Don, who aggressively ignored them and relied on intuition. He backed and turned impatiently, snarling at Gary and swearing evenly.

The familiar flashing blue light of a car belting through a cross street to the right resolved it and Don accelerated and followed.

With the siren dribbling into detumescence Don eased the car into the kerb behind a rough line of stationary police vehicles in the tree-lined residential street. There must have been a dozen or more of them: several divisional vans, two yellow Traffic Operations sedans, a couple of unmarked cars and even a Dog

Squad van whose Alsatian was yelping with frustration at being kept from the excitement by the mesh of its cage.

Two stationary cars had left their revolving blue lights on and the narrow street throbbed surrealistically. The stroboscopic flashes illuminated the milling police members and the little clumps of neighbours in dressing gowns and pyjamas who watched with morbid fascination.

Three young bucks lay face down on the asphalt in the centre of the road, wrists handcuffed awkwardly across the small of their backs. One had blood trickling from a gash on his cheek bone. Gary spotted Christine among the police clustering around. She seemed strained but unhurt. Myxo, beside her, had a ripped shirt which fluttered grotesquely in the gusts of light rain but he displayed no obvious physical damage.

The Preston divisional van, parked at a forty-five degree angle to the gutter, rocked on its springs like a jelly. A drunken kid was trying to kick his way out of the maddeningly constricting cage. Gary glanced apprehensively at Don as the kid's shouts escalated into hysterical screams. 'He'll do some damage,' said Don, 'but more to his feet and knuckles than to the arc-mesh grill.' A middle-aged senior constable strolled across and stood at the rear of the van impassively training his torch on the occupant. The kid shrieked with impotent anger and renewed his kicking.

They mingled with the other police members, trading snatches of information. Apparently it was a routine job which had turned sour. Christine had messed up the radio work – underestimating the situation and being reluctant to lose face with her male colleagues by calling for assistance – and the VKC operator had been obliged to take the initiative. Fortunately he had plenty of units close by and they had reached there before Myxo took too much of a pummelling. Five arrests had been made and the remainder of the pack had retreated to the block of flats where the party was continuing.

Somewhere glass was breaking. There were shouts from a constable waving his torch in the darkened vestibule of the flats. Brawling had broken out again. Most of the police milling around the vehicles moved off across the lawn in a ragged group. Gary followed eagerly, drawing the baton from his right-hand pocket and looping the leather thong around his wrist.

Don stayed behind with two members guarding the handcuffed youths and keeping the spectators away from them. A couple of teenage girls huddled together on the footpath sobbing hysterically.

The show of strength quelled the fight rapidly and fifteen or twenty police filtered back into the circle of throbbing lights from the cluster of vehicles. Gary and two other constables half carried and half dragged two more handcuffed youths.

Back at the station Don assisted where he could. Because he had been on the periphery of the fracas, he was not the 'informant' in any of the charges being laid and was thus not directly involved in the paperwork. The station was a chaos of shouting prisoners and grimly tired police members milling in and out of the interview rooms. The kid in the back of the divisional van had emerged with boots and fists flailing and had been batoned into whimpering semi-consciousness.

By two-thirty a.m. the place had settled into some sort of order. Two of the prisoners had been processed and lodged in the cells and records of interview with the others were being typed in the four interview rooms. The foyer was still a noisy throng of witnesses, relatives and police members bustling in and out. But in the rear of the station, where Don stood, it was relatively quiet – just the clack of typewriters and occasional outburst of angry questions.

For Don the shift had finished half-an-hour ago but he would certainly not go home until it was all sorted out. The others would eventually drift down to the mess room for the usual post-mortem yarning over coffee. In any case it was getting on to three a.m.: his wife would be asleep and there would be little welcome in the darkened house. Gary had finished processing his offender some time before and had disappeared into the throng in the foyer. Don glanced out of the window. The rain had dissolved into sullen cloud tinged by the reflection of the amber street lights.

Feeling a little useless, he wandered into the empty mess room and made a cup of tea with a tea bag and the barely boiling water. It tasted awful. He sat at the Laminex table moodily toying with the sugar spoon. 'What did it all achieve?' he pondered, 'The bucks were drunk to the point of mindless, sullen hatred. They would respond to questioning with aggression – physical or verbal – and the police would respond in the same way. Punches would be thrown, blood spilt and humanity lost – on both sides.'

He put down the teaspoon and shook his head with cynical resignation: his train of thought had been interrupted, with the perfect timing of a well-scripted play, by the noise of scuffling in the interview room across the corridor. That distinctive noise – somewhere between a 'whack' and a 'thump' – of fist colliding with flesh was unmistakable.

He stared into his lukewarm cup of tea.

Gary appeared, cheeks flushed with excitement, and sat down opposite him.

'What's wrong, Don, you look bloody miserable? Did you cop a few hits in the soft parts during the punch-up?'

'No, mate, just thinking.'

'About what?'

'About the whole stupid, no-win game!' he snapped with an intensity which he had not intended to convey but he was now committed to continue. 'About the pointless "Us versus Them" business. These bucks don't know or care about you or Myxo or Christine or me: they just react to the uniform ... the ...' he fumbled for words. 'A sort of symbol – a symbol of authority. They lash out: we kick back. We've got six of them in the cells – big deal! So six bucks front a Magistrates Court where they'll get a piss-weak sermon and a good behaviour bond. They'll come away from it whingeing about the way they were treated at the station and conveniently forgetting who started it all; and they'll boast to the younger kids and the whole fucking game continues.'

Gary fidgeted uneasily, as he always did at Don's occasional philosophising.

Don's mind registered it – sermons would change nothing – and he tried to reorganise himself into the usual banter with Gary.

'Anyway,' he said, 'what have you been up to? I thought you had finished the paperwork on your arrest a couple of hours ago?'

'Oh, yeah. But we really fixed up that little cunt. He was the one who tried to kick me in the balls. He's in the cell over there.'

'Yeah but that was a while ago?'

'Yes, but his girlfriend showed up later – a little slut of about fifteen. She came around all weepy and wanted to see him. So I told her he was being held at Northcote station.'

'You what?'

'I pissed her off to Northcote. They must have given her a rough time there because by the time she got back here she was bawling like hell.'

'And what the fuck did you do then?' Don snapped with rising anger.

Gary beamed. 'I told her some bullshit: told her that she couldn't see him because we had information that he was involved in sex offences with little girls. Jesus, did she go ape! Went hysterical. Wailed until some civilian put her in a taxi and sent her home.'

Don's guts knotted, his right fist clenched. He wanted to smash the plasticine blandness of Gary's face. He lurched to his feet, knuckles white, and then swayed there, feeling foolish. Sermons would change nothing, nor more blind punches. Irrelevantly his mind dredged up only the memory of his father's wall clock which made an ineffectual whirring noise, instead of the boom of the definitive hour of the day, when the old man had forgotten to wind it. He sank back into his chair.

'Don, Don, are you all right?'

'Yeah,' he said, 'don't take any notice of me. It's been a long shift. I'm getting twitchy.'

Gary made a pot of tea.

'Don,' he said, 'I don't really understand all that stuff you talk about "Us and Them". We had to back-up Christine, didn't we?'

30

6

THE TRUTH,
THE WHOLE TRUTH AND. . .

Silence, all stand! These sittings
of the Darwin Magistrates
Court are now resumed. Let all
persons having business before
this honourable court draw
near, give their attention and
they shall be heard. God save
the Queen! Be seated.

Thank you, Constable. Police
Prosecutor?

Sergeant O'Callaghan again,
Your Worship. I believe we are
ready to continue with the
committal-for-trial proceedings
on the alleged river-bank
murder. Your Worship will
recall that we were obliged to
adjourn yesterday after having
some difficulty. . .

Yes, indeed.

. . . some difficulty in eliciting
from the Defendant whether he
wished to enter a plea of guilty,
to enter a plea of not guilty or
to reserve his defence. I believe
that Your Worship is now
prepared to deem it a 'reserved
defence'. . .

No damned alternative.

... and for me to proceed with
calling the Crown witnesses?

Yes, Sergeant. How many?

Eight, Your Worship.

How many?

Eight, Sir. All of them
Aboriginal aged pensioners
from the river-bank camp who
claim to have observed the
alleged brawl and who are
eager to give evidence. It could
. . . er . . .take some days, Your
Worship.

Oh, my god. Constable, can't
you do anything about that
damned air-conditioner?

Well, no, Your Worship. It's
running at full throttle now.

Very well. Proceed, Sergeant.

Thank you, Sir. My first
witness is Lightning Harry of
the Katherine river-bank camp.

Good god, Sergeant, don't you
have his proper tribal name?

Well, no, Sir. He doesn't speak
particularly good English and
we've managed to get his
mother's family name, his skin-
group name and his uncle's
tribal name but . . . well . . .
well, everyone in Katherine
calls him 'Lightning Harry'.

Very well. Constable, call the
witness.

Yes, Your Worship. Lightning
Harry! Lightning Harry!
Lightning Harry! Appears,
Your Worship.

Thank you. Just take the stand
please.

        Eh?

The stand, Witness, the stand.
Oh, just go into *that* – that
wooden box-thing. Thank you.
Your name?

        Harold Nabaljari, Boss. My
        uncle is Alphonse of Oenpelli
        but he died when I was a little
        feller.

Er . . . yes. But you are also
known as 'Lightning Harry'?

        Bloody oath! You come from
        the Katherine district?

Well . . . er . . . no. Now,
Mr Harry . . .

        '*Lightning* Harry', Boss.

Yes, quite so. Now, Mr . . . er,
now, Witness, do you wish to
give your evidence under oath
or on affirmation?

        Yes, Boss.

No, Witness, you don't
understand. I am offering you
an alternative: you may swear
on the bible . . .

        No way, Boss! My cousin in
        Alice Springs got two weeks
        for swearing at a magistrate.

No, Witness, it's a matter of
under which constraints you
give your evidence . . .

        Yes, Boss. He killed him, but.

What?

        Him. The bloke in the other
        box. I saw him kill the dead

feller. Swinging a bloody great
piece of timber . . .

Witness, we cannot hear your
testimony until you are
properly attested or sworn.
Now do you wish to simply
make a solemn promise to tell
the truth or do you wish to
make that promise while
holding a bible?

Yes, thank you, Boss.

Thank *you*. Constable can't you
do *anything* abut that damned
silly air-conditioner?

It's running flat out already,
Boss . . . I mean, Your Worship.

Very well, we'll start again.
Now, Harry . . .

'*Lightning* Harry', Boss.

Yes, Witness. But you
understand that there are
certain rules concerning the
giving of evidence?

Oh, Jesus, yes, Boss. And it
was a bloody big stick that he
belted him with.

I cannot hear that testimony
yet. First, Witness, I am obliged
by the rules of evidence to
ascertain whether you wish to
give your evidence as a
Christian or under an
affirmation. The choice is
yours.

Whatever you think's a fair
thing, Boss.

Please, Witness. Basically all I
need to know is *are* you a
Christian?

> Oh, Jesus, no, Boss: I'm a
> pensioner!

Oh my god. Constable, would
you adjourn the court for the
morning tea break?

> Yes, Your Worship. Silence, all
> stand! This honourable court is
> now adjourned. God Save the
> Queen!

7

THE HOUSE-WARMING

It was not difficult for Ken to settle in to barracks life. He did like his parents and the old house behind Dad's milk bar in Brunswick. But the elder brother had gone overseas a couple of years ago, the younger sister had married last June and he was isolated. God knows, there was not much conversation a lone son could make over those evening meals with Dad mumbling endlessly about the price of petrol or postage stamps and Mum mindlessly agreeing with him. Ken's bedroom had been sparse and impersonal – a bed, a desk, a couple of football posters on the wall – and his life had really revolved around his job and the bunch of mates who met each evening in the saloon bar of 'The Sarah Sands'. The environment of the Recruit Academy was not qualitatively different. The room allocated to him was furnished in much the same way as his old one at home, the recruit squad replaced the bunch of mates, and 'The Snake Pit' – the wet canteen at the Academy – replaced 'The Sarah Sands'.

The recruit course consisted of five months of live-in training at the huge monastery in Melbourne's eastern suburbs that had once been the principal seminary for training priests. (Apparently religion had been going through a recession and law and order was the growth industry; with a dwindling number of recruits to the priesthood, the Church had shrewdly sold to the government the cavernous building known as 'Corpus Christi' – now known colloquially as 'Coppers Christi'.) Ken would return to his parents' home each weekend but, after the first few weeks, found himself spending much of the Saturdays with fellow squad members at the football. Even weekend contact with civilian mates imperceptibly became less frequent.

Of the squad of thirty recruits, about a quarter had transferred directly from the Police Cadet Corps on reaching the age of eighteen years and three months. Ken liked a couple of them – young Snowy with his open grin and endless repertoire of ingenious dirty jokes, and Mocca with his shyness and stumbling honesty – but was suspicious of the rest. As cadets, they had been put into uniform immediately upon leaving school at sixteen or seventeen and had lived in the semi-military atmosphere of the Cadet Academy in the city until reaching the minimum age to join a recruit squad. Ken sensed a certain arrogance and narrowness.

Another quarter were women. Their activities – especially their real or imagined sexual activities – occupied an inordinate proportion of the conversation of the group of mates with whom Ken drank regularly in 'The Snake Pit'. He happily joined in the gossip and speculation but in fact had little to do with them. Their sleeping quarters were out of bounds to male recruits ('But only in theory!' Snowy announced one morning with a triumphant grin and a highly exaggerated account of his exploits of the previous evening); they rarely joined Ken's group in 'The Snake Pit' and tended to keep to themselves in the dining hall. This left only the classroom, which was, after all, the least significant part of those twenty weeks of training.

The third quarter had joined at the minimum age – direct from school or the dole – and the remainder were older recruits coming from an odd variety of occupations.

Ken was in fact only twenty-three but tended to be identified with this older group. He spent most of his time with Lofty Spence, who had done nine years as a corporal in the Australian Army. By the end of the first week they were known as 'Mutt and Jeff' in the squad: a reference to Ken's tall, angular seriousness and to Lofty's short, rotund joviality. A standing joke was that Lofty had bribed the Medical Examiner with one of his Vietnam medals to ignore the five-feet eight-and-a-half inches height requirement for a police recruit.

The other nickname which Ken acquired was 'The Padre'. This had begun when young Mocca, the shy cadet fresh from his family's wheat block in the Wimmera, had won himself a dose of gonorrhoea in his first independent foray into the night life of the big city. Mocca had been terrified by the symptoms and Ken had tried to reassure him. Later, in the noisy sessions in 'The Snake Pit', there were many ribald comments – sarcastic but with an edge of admiration – about Ken's gentle efforts to explain the facts to Mocca, to get him to the clinic in Fitzroy and, above all, to make sure that the idiot didn't do anything which would bring it to the attention of the training staff. The nickname stuck.

*   *   *   *

On graduation they were scattered to various training stations but the four of them maintained a ritual of meeting at a city pub each weekend or when their rest days coincided. It was during one of those sessions, towards the end of their first year out, that Snowy had floated the idea of them getting together and renting a house in the inner suburbs. Ken smirked knowingly: he had heard, on several occasions at the Police Club, the story of Snowy's landlady threatening eviction after being woken by orgasmic groans coming from the back bedroom. But there was a certain logic to it, especially when Lofty chimed in with some arithmetic on the cost of rent and electricity split equally between four or five mates.

Ken was lined up for a vacancy at Northcote station. Nothing of course was official: he still had to pass the probationary constables' exam and put in for the vacancy which was open to any constable and subject to appeal. But, unless some unknown constable with seniority crawled out of the woodwork, he had a good chance of getting the position and had already spoken to the senior sergeant who ran the sub-district. He went back there and mentioned Snowy's suggestion. The senior sergeant was known as 'Ocker' (though not to his face by probationary constables) because of his heavy Yorkshire accent. Ocker listened with that studied reserve punctuated by sarcastic obscenities which is the stock in trade of any senior sergeant dealing with an enthusiastic young constable. He suggested that Ken contact a particular estate agent.

The next day Ken dialled the number which the senior sergeant had scrawled on a scrap of paper and was surprised – almost flattered – that the agent knew his name and had prepared a list of places for rent.

He was happy with the first place the estate agent showed him: a battered, rather drab weatherboard house in a narrow street off High Street, Northcote. He tried unsuccessfully to reach Snowy or Lofty by phone from the agent's office – they were probably on night shift or rest day – and ended up signing the lease himself. It was another two days before he actually met up with them in the Police Club and explained the details of the lease, but they were happy to accept his judgment. A week later Snowy and Lofty moved in. Mocca got around to it in the next month.

The house ran well. It was bare and lacking in the warmth of a home that revolved around children or permanent relationships. No-one got around to putting up curtains or hanging pictures (apart from a painfully obscene centrefold which Snowy taped above the gas stove and to which Mocca added a moustache with a felt-tip pen) but it suited them. It was tatty and spartan but with a certain macho conviviality. Its atmosphere was not very different from that of a station mess room on night shift.

*   *   *   *

'The senior sergeant wants to see you.'

Ken frowned. Ocker conducted most discussions with his men over coffee in the mess room or over the watch-house counter and it was a little unusual to be summoned to his office, especially as Ken was just signing off from day shift. He tapped on the glass partition. 'Bob says you want to see me, Sarge?'

'Yeah,' he muttered without looking up from his writing, 'sit down – got a complaint file against you.'

Christ, a complaint file! Ken lowered himself into the chair in front of the senior sergeant's desk, frantically searching his mind for what they could have on him. He was, as far as he knew, 'clean'. There was that loud-mouthed young buck last week who had shouted suggestions about the sex life of the senior connie's wife when they were questioning him at the station and had, as a result, 'slipped on the stairs leading to the cells' and incurred some bruising. But, Jesus, he was a docket-head who had done something like double the number of burglaries which they had actually charged him with and was hardly in a position to lay a complaint!

Ocker continued to write impassively.

Ken's mind frenetically flipped through memories of the last couple of months. There was that silly bitch in the Mercedes who had taken exception to his request that she produce her licence after damned-near wiping out a couple of kids on a pedestrian crossing. He had been nearing the end of a heavy day shift and she had been shrilly and unsubtly trying to communicate that she was a hard-pressed career woman nearing the end of a heavy day of social commitments. He may have used the word 'bitch' – he could not remember – but he had not booked her. He shifted anxiously in the chair.

'Aw, for chrissake, son, they're not going to hang you – it's not a "B11" matter.' Ocker said it without glancing up.

Ken relaxed a little and reorganised his thinking, sorting out the fact that a complaint of criminal conduct would be investigated by the hated B11 – the Bureau of Internal Investigation – while a middling complaint would be checked by an officer of the Division and a minor matter would be passed to his station senior sergeant. He slumped with relief but his mind moved back into higher gear as he rechecked memories of minor matters which they could hang on him.

The senior sergeant rubber-stamped and initialled the report he had been reading, closed the file and slid it to the side of the desk. For the first time he looked into Ken's face.

'You rent a house with a couple of other young connies?'

Ken nodded dumbly.

'Who cuts the lawn?'

Ken stared blankly and mumbled: 'I organise that'.

'Yes, I know that, you fuckwit, but who actually cuts the bloody stuff?'

With a mixture of confusion and disbelief, Ken explained that a local kid came around once a fortnight to do it. Baffled by the question, he flailed about trying to provide whatever information the senior sergeant was looking for. He explained about the number of people in the house, the size of the lawn, the way he had met the kid on a routine divisional van call to clear a pack of kids from the park . . .

'Yes,' Ocker intervened, 'and that was the kid you put in a "cautioning recommendation" for on the 276?'

Ken's mind steadied and he tried to piece it together. Yes, there were grounds for charging the kid with Malicious Damage but on the '276' – the yellow, one-page pro-forma reporting an alleged offence by a juvenile – he had ticked the box which recommended that he be summoned to appear before a police officer with his parents to be 'cautioned', rather than required to appear at the Childrens Court on a criminal charge. Ken remembered that some derision had been expressed by other members of the station staff. The Cautioning Programme applied only to first offenders and, although the kid had no formal prior convictions, he was known to police as a cheeky little trouble-maker from a Housing Commission family who would not normally be given that privilege. At the time the senior sergeant had, in his laconic way, queried Ken's recommendation but had let it pass.

Now Ken found himself blurting out a confused description of the incident which had occurred some months ago. He explained how the kid had left school but was not eligible for the dole; how he turned out to be not as bad as he looked; how Ken had bumped into him a few weeks later and suggested that he try to pick up a few bucks by cutting lawns; how the kid had been wary and Ken had suggested their place as a start. In fact, the kid had shown up regularly at the house – at first nervous and surly, but with growing confidence – and now came every two weeks and even shyly had a cup of coffee with them when the job was done. He seemed to like Snowy, who was trying, ineffectually, to talk him into looking for an apprenticeship. (He also seemed to enjoy some of Snowy's more outlandish stories but Ken did not mention that.)

Ocker listened impassively. 'One of your friendly neighbours wrote an anonymous letter to B11,' he grunted, 'alleging that you are standing over the local juvenile delinquents and using them to get your housework done.'

Ken tensed with anger. He checked the immediate impulse to explain that he was scrupulously paying the kid the going rate for lawn mowing. Nor could he explain that the money usually came out of his own pocket as Lofty and the others were never well enough organised to keep the housekeeping kitty replenished. And he certainly could not explain that the kid seemed to be responding to their fumbling attempts to allow him some dignity as the senior sergeant would certainly snap: 'What are you trying to be, son – a copper or a social worker?'

Instead he simply said: 'That's bullshit, Sarge. One kid does some part-time work for us and we pay him at the going rate'.

'OK', Ocker's eyes blinked the unspoken but clear indication that he believed him completely, 'But piss the kid off. We've got enough anonymous complaints on our hands without spending time on little old ladies who believe you are organising a white slave trade to get your fucking lawn cut. Cut it yourself.' Ocker said it without malice or destructive suspicion. But it was the unambiguous command of an old, experienced senior sergeant directing a young constable.

Ken signed off and walked home. Without bothering to change out of uniform, he made a cup of coffee and sat at the table in the bare kitchen in quiet, controlled anger – not at the senior sergeant but at the petty, paranoid world of 'them'.

Snowy arrived home noisily. 'Christ, Padre, you're a miserable looking bastard! A long, lean streak of misery. But don't worry, me old mate, we're going to cheer you up. We're going to have a house-warming party!'

'A "house-warming party"? Oh, for chrissake, Snowy, we've been living in this bloody house for nearly a year now.'

42

'You've got no soul, Padre. Music, soft lights, gaiety is what you need!' He slipped into his camp routine, waving his hands and fluttering his eyelids outrageously.

Ken chuckled. He guessed – quite correctly as it turned out – that Snowy had discovered another couple of bored trainee nurses from the nearby Austin Hospital.

*   *   *   *

Somehow it was Ken who ended up buying the grog, cheese and biscuits the following Saturday. Perhaps it was because he was the only one of them who was rostered for a clear rest day then. But he still grinned sheepishly when Lofty arrived at the close of day shift to catch him slicing cabana sausage and arranging cashew nuts in saucers. Lofty made some wisecrack about Ken making a perfect husband for some lucky girl and Ken swore at him cheerfully.

The house was stark and bare and the girls would be civilians. But Lofty was helpful: he had borrowed a stack of cassettes for the tape deck and even set to work sweeping out the grubby kitchen. When he produced a packet of air-freshener and placed it on the toilet cistern Ken returned the wisecrack about house-trained potential husbands and they laughed and opened a beer.

Somewhere around eight o'clock the four girls arrived with Snowy and Mocca, all of them a little giggly as they had met by arrangement in the lounge of the 'Royal' some hours before. Drinks were opened and the tape deck turned up.

Ken grinned inwardly as he watched Snowy telling yarns of his police experiences. If anything like half of them were true he would have to be a detective chief inspector by now. But Snowy was a charmer: his grin signalled that you weren't expected to believe it all – just enjoy the fluency – and the girls loved him.

Ken, slightly more sober than the rest, observed the unspoken sifting process of a party as the group of noisy individuals gradually coagulates into pairs. Snowy, of course, ended up monopolising the attention of Maria, the vivacious girl with large brown eyes who was by far the most attractive one. Mocca hung around Cheryl, attentively getting her drinks, and Lofty engaged the dumpy red-head in long, whispered conversations.

Ken noted ruefully that he ended up more or less paired with Tracy, who was superficially sexy in appearance but whose conversation consisted of a non-stop stream of trivia about television shows and movies. It became more vacuous with each rum and coke. She loved crime films she said, and adored policemen.

Towards one a.m. the combination of noise generated by the tape deck, the shrill laughter of the red-head and the gleeful shouts of Mocca made all conversation unintelligible. Tracy continued to chatter on and Ken nodded politely to give the impression that he was listening as he opened the second bottle of scotch. He rarely drank spirits and was becoming conscious of a weary but pleasant stillness in his limbs. He gazed at her lips with clinical passivity. They never kept still but maintained a sheen of moisture. The others were dancing frenetically. He glanced up to observe Snowy and Maria chuckling with childlike delight as Snowy moved into an inept but enthusiastic attempt at a disco dance routine. Maria laughed clearly, tossing her head so that the long black hair swept back over her shoulders and, in rhythm with the music, began to unbutton her blouse. She was, Ken guessed, of Italian extraction and had pointed nipples circled by wide rings of brown on small, tight breasts. His genitals stirred and grumbled.

The noise and laughter increased. Lofty's girl stripped down to her panties and tried to outdo Maria and Snowy in disco dancing, her bulbous breasts jiggling.

Mocca's self-conscious groping with the frizzy-haired girl on the couch was suddenly lost in happy, drunken explicitness as he shed a lot of inhibitions – along with his jeans, removed with the giggling aid of his partner when his shirt jammed the zipper – and slipped into a panting, graceless missionary position.

Ken chuckled and ambled out to the back lawn to piss under the lemon tree. He had a momentary experience of clear night sky – amber street lights silhouetting the beech trees in the park and the distant wail of a police siren – before Tracy joined him. She threw her arms around his chest as he fumbled to re-zip his fly. He kissed her awkwardly, pawing her large breasts tightly encased in an angular brassiere. She was fairly drunk. He sensed her growing excitement as they kissed and fondled. She had unclipped her bra before it dawned on her that they were in the middle of the back yard. 'Let's go inside', she said eagerly.

They sprawled on a bean bag, momentarily conscious of the contrast between the silence of the back yard and the noisy clutter of the living room – overflowing ashtrays, littered bottles and the tape deck belting out rock music relentlessly. Snowy and Maria had disappeared, presumably to the bedroom. Mocca and the frizzy-haired girl were opening another bottle of beer, giggling like a pair of school kids at their gleefully flaunted nakedness. Lofty and the red-head were in a heavy clinch on the sofa, oblivious of anyone else.

He lit a cigarette and Tracy curled into his arms. Somewhere, deep within his fogged brain, a thought stirred: the awareness that he was not really turned on by it all. Christ, I'm going camp or something! She was stroking his thigh and he could feel an erection straining against his jeans, but somehow it was not right. Mentally he groped for some definition of how he felt. He glanced over at Lofty and his girl who were totally unaware of anything but each other. That should, he thought with drunken deliberation, be about as erotic as you can get – her bum was towards him, legs splayed and pubic hair glistening, as she crouched over Lofty sucking him off – but the only emotion which Ken could identify within his revolving brain was one of mild embarrassment. 'Aw, shit,' he mumbled, lurching to his feet, 'let's go to bed.'

Tracy followed. Ironically she perceived his move as the final surrender to her seductiveness – roughly the opposite of what Ken was expressing.

But, drunk or not, he was a healthy young recruit and fatalistically he pumped his way to a sobbing orgasm with her in the sparse room with its football posters and unshaded light bulb.

8

FOX

I could never fully relax over a beer with Les. It was not just that he was a creaking, bitter old bastard – god knows, that would describe a large number of mates whose company I thoroughly enjoy – it was something to do with our relationship. Something about the role he seemed to cast me in.

Piecing together odds and ends of comments scattered over many months of drinking at the 'Napier', I gathered that he had done a pretty long stretch in Pentridge on manslaughter, but no-one ever elaborated on it. He had been on the pension for years – Invalid Pension and then, over the past seven years or so, the Aged Pension. He survived with the limping craftiness of a moulting old fox. He lived in a tiny flat provided by the Brotherhood of St Laurence for 'socially-disadvantaged elderly persons'. Within that world, his survival skills included the manipulation of the middle-class social workers who guaranteed his 'meals on wheels' and the roof over his head. And it was this that made me uneasy.

But he was hard to avoid. 'The Napier', opposite Fitzroy Town Hall, would open at ten and Les would stalk in at five past ten each morning, buy a pot and spend the next four hours sitting stiffly at the tiny Laminex table by the door of the saloon bar. I was often the only other customer.

He always wore the gaberdine overcoat and the high-crowned hat, which he never removed. It occurred to me once that it would be difficult to give a physical description of Les as he had such an anonymous demeanour: the skinny ankles and bulbous beer-gut of a bloke in his seventies, the expressionless face and the crumpled coat which never changed, winter or summer. I had never seen what sort of hair he had under that hat.

Inevitably in the near-empty bar, one got yarning. He could not read or write and, somehow, I ended up writing letters for him at his dictation: letters to the Department of Social Security, the Repatriation Department, or whatever welfare organisation or government agency he was grizzling to at the time. It was not a role I enjoyed.

To make it worse, the Brotherhood of St Laurence flats happened to be next door to the grimy little house which I had rented in Moore Street. Les would get bored with the hygienic isolation of his trim welfare flat and would rap on my window and come in and spend the afternoon yarning over beers. His etiquette was flawless and he always kept a count of the beers consumed, returning on alternate days with the precise number of stubbies in return.

You couldn't be rude to him – god knows he had been kicking around the traps when I was still in nappies – but I sometimes wished that he would go away. I had made a clean break with the criminal justice game: no more hassles with the coppers, no more entanglements with mates on both sides of the law. I just wanted to merge back into my old world of Fitzroy as a respectable, invisible citizen trying to make a quid as a freelance commercial artist working out of the front room of the little place in Moore Street. Of course I never told Les any of this but I had the eerie sensation that the old bugger could intuitively smell out an ex social worker.

*   *   *   *

Tap, tap, tap.

'OK, Les, be with you in a sec.' The door of the front room had been nailed up and painted over years ago and one had to retreat back through the jumbled living room, around the tiny kitchen and then forward along the passageway of corrugated iron to reach the only door which opened on to the street.

He was agitated.

'Rod, I need a hand . . . I've got a bloody great crate that fell off the back of a truck . . . gotta get it into your place quick!'

'Oh for chrissake, Les, I'm a straight citizen these days. I can't help you with hot stuff!'

'But it just fell off the back of a truck.'

'Yeah, yeah, yeah.'

'No, I mean a *truck* . . . you know, a real one . . . four wheels and all that.'

He tugged me by the arm onto the pavement and pointed across the road to the intersection of Moore and Gore Streets. There was a big pine crate askew in the gutter. He chattered excitedly: a truck had braked hard to avoid a sedan hurtling through the crossroads and had then accelerated violently, toppling the crate from the rear of the tray. Godhelpus, for once he might be speaking the truth! I had seen similar mishaps at that dangerous intersection.

Eventually we manhandled it across the road and into the passageway of my house. It seemed to weigh a ton and we could only roll it, end over end, like two geriatric dung beetles.

I got the claw-hammer from the kitchen and prised off a couple of slats. Shiny machinery components packed in grease and stuff like heavy silver paper.

'Christ, that must be worth a mint!' he muttered over my shoulder.

I unwrapped more. They appeared to be hydraulic components – pistons, valves and switch-gear – probably for bulldozers or heavy trucks. They were machined intricately, polished stainless steel, the glistening grease encasing their precision.

'Right,' said Les, 'we'll leave 'em here while I make the rounds.'

'Hey, hang on, mate. You can't go flogging this stuff around the pubs. It's complicated hydraulic gear – not the sort of stuff you can off-load in a pub.'

'But what do you reckon it's worth?'

I squinted at the glistening packages. 'A couple of thousand, I suppose.'

He straightened his gaberdine overcoat and turned towards the door.

'Les, for chrissake, it's all stamped with serial numbers – they would track it down to you in a couple of days.'

'What did you say it's worth?'

'Oh, Christ!' I cradled my head in my arms on the crate. 'Les, Les, Les, can't you see that this is specialised, expensive gear – word would get around the traps – and with your prior convictions. . .'

'It's a lot of money but.'

I took a deep breath. 'Look, Les, I'm not your bloody keeper, mate. You're a bit older than me and I can't tell you what to do. But, for chrissake, you *can't* flog this gear!'

He eyed me carefully.

Desperately I dropped my voice to the stern but soothing tone used by that lecturer in Social Work at Melbourne University many years ago. 'Les,' I said, 'it is obvious that you are going to get yourself into more strife than a pregnant nun if you try to hawk this stuff. There are, however, realistic alternatives.' I cleared my throat. 'You could, for example, go to the firm which manufactured the gear – the address is stamped on the side of the crate – and explain how you found it. It is worth a considerable amount of money and, if they note that you are a pensioner, they would surely provide a small reward. It might not be much but it is, after all, a windfall and it leaves you with the satisfaction of having done the Right Thing and there are no hassles with the wallopers.'

He pondered in silence for several minutes, once again straightened the gaberdine overcoat and turned to the door.

*　　　　*　　　　*　　　　*

'Ring, ring, ring' on the useless doorbell of the front room.

It was obviously neither Les nor any of my mates, all of whom understood the routine of tapping on the window by the nailed-up door. I made the circuitous trek to the door which opened on to the street.

'I've come for the stuff.'

49

'What stuff?' I said with the natural caution of anyone being addressed by an aggressive young man in an expensive business suit.

'You know damned well what I mean. We've paid up.'

I adopted the pained look of bewilderment which I normally use when confronted by questioning constables. This time, though, the bewilderment was more or less genuine.

Silence hung for several seconds over the tableau we made standing in motionless confrontation at the open doorway. Eventually he snapped: 'Look, we've been through it all with your mate: how the crate "fell off the back of a truck", how he wanted to return it to us, how one of his heavy crim mates from Fitzroy had stepped in, taken it off him and hidden it away. I've got to admit that he would make a damned good Indonesian shop-keeper: it took an hour of negotiation before he would tell us who had the stuff and we ended up paying $40 cash for your address. *Now* can I have the stuff?'

There was nothing I could say. The crate was so heavy that we had manoeuvred it only a few inches inside the door and I had the back of my knees braced against it. I grinned weakly and parted my knees with virginal innocence.

He beckoned to a couple of blokes in overalls who moved in. They loaded it on to the back off a truck and clambered aboard. The young man in the business suit paused, turned to me and snarled: 'And the next time you thieving bastards try a conspiracy like this on us, we'll bring in the police!'

Closing the door, I threaded my way back through the maze to the front room, scooping a beer from the kitchen fridge on the way. The hell with it! I never was any bloody good as a social worker anyway.

Besides, Les, with his strict sense of what is proper, would insist on providing forty dollars' worth of beer for our afternoon sessions for the next couple of weeks . . .

9

SENTENCE

In Australasian courts the legal doctrine concerning 'provocation' as a defence to a charge of murder is complex. It is buried in the convoluted reasoning of many case law rulings in which the judges have struggled to impose some sort of legal logic on to the basic human response to someone who has killed without cold-blooded premeditation but in the 'heat of passion' after being provoked beyond endurance. In the case of *Johnson v R* before the High Court of Australia ((1976) 11 ALR 23), Chief Justice Barwick observed that four themes seem to run through all the case law precedents over the centuries. First, that the victim must have acted in such a way that could provoke any 'ordinary person' to lose self-control (*Bedder v DPP* [1954] 2 All ER 801). Second, that the killer himself had indeed lost self-control (*Moffa v R* (1977) 13 ALR 225). Third, that the killer had not exacted revenge after a 'cooling off' period but had acted spontaneously in immediate response to the provocation (*Parker v R* (1964) 111 CLR 665 (PC)). Fourth, that by attacking the victim with the intention to kill or at least inflict serious injury, the killer had reacted in a way in which an ordinary person could have reacted (*Enright v R* [1961] VR 663, 669).[2] In Papua New Guinea the legislature has attempted to codify the basics of the doctrine in section 504 of the Papua New Guinea Criminal Code, which permits 'provocation' to include, inter alia:

> Any wrongful act or insult of such nature as to be likely, when done
> ... in the presence of an ordinary person to another person who is

---

2   Some recent cases have significantly modified and refined the doctrine of
     provocation. See, for example, *The Queen v R* (1981) 28 SASR 321, and especially
     the ruling of the High Court in *Stingel v R* (1990) 97 ALR 1. However I am
     summarising above the major themes in Common Law as they stood in 1972.

under his immediate care, or to whom he stands in a conjugal, parental, filial or fraternal relation of master and servant, to deprive him of the power of self-control, and to induce him to assault the person by whom the act or insult is done or offered.

If it is accepted that there was provocation beyond endurance, the accused is not acquitted: the charge is merely reduced from 'murder' to 'manslaughter'. In practice, the sentences imposed for either murder or manslaughter are not always significantly different: the reduction of the charge simply allows the trial judge to impose a less severe sentence if he or she so desires. Thus the net effect of all this complex legal doctrine is, in the end, contingent on the decisiveness of the particular judge. Judges tend to be cautious in imposing light sentences on homicide charges, as a Crown appeal against 'excessive leniency' in sentencing can indeed be a blot on the copy book of an aspiring judge. Much depends on the courage of the individual judge. I observed the decisiveness of a very courageous judge in an obscure, unreported murder trial in the Eastern Highlands Province of Papua New Guinea in 1972.

The courtroom in Goroka is a tatty little place: small windows of louvred glass illuminating a bald wooden floor on which are scattered a few irregular rows of plastic chairs of garish pink for the spectators. The 'bar table' for the barristers is an ungainly kitchen table. On either side stand two wooden podia – the 'dock' and the 'witness box'. The 'bench' for the judge is a wooden desk on a dais raised six or seven inches to give some semblance of the architecture of a British court of law. On the wall behind the judge's chair hangs a slightly faded photograph of the Sovereign Monarch of this colony and the Fountainhead of its Law – Elizabeth II – encased in a frame of fly-spotted glass.

The judge, in wig and scarlet criminal-jurisdiction robes, entered, bowed to the assembled persons and took his seat. As his Associate, I occupied a small plastic desk situated in front of the dais, facing the bar table. Feeling, as usual, slightly ridiculous in lawyers gown and bibs, I intoned: 'These sittings of the Supreme Court of Papua New Guinea holden at Goroka are now in session. Let all persons having business before this honourable court draw near, give their attention and they shall be heard. God save the Queen!'

After the two barristers – prosecution and defence – had been formally acknowledged by the judge and the two interpreters had been sworn in, the accused was escorted into the courtroom by two prison warders.

Yaubriki took his place in the dock, dressed only in the blue-and-white stripe *laplap* of a remand prisoner. The lobes of both his ears had been ritually pierced many years ago and now hung in dangles of leathery skin. He was very old and frail yet there was an indefinable aura of dignity about him. In the plane on the way to Goroka I had read the court file. Statements of witnesses contained in the 'depositions' – the written record of evidence given at the committal for trial proceedings – suggested that he was a 'Big Man' in his village: a revered elder who had been a battle commander in the incessant tribal warfare which had only recently been lessened by the imposition of white rule. Now, it seemed, he had accepted new times and old age and lived quietly in the village, caring for his herd of pigs and his one remaining aged wife. He spoke only Melpa, a little Tok Pisin – the creole language of Papua New Guinea – and no English.

I commenced the ritual by rising and intoning: 'Yaubriki Ana you stand charged that on 27 July 1972 in the village of Kefeno you did wilfully murder one Zorike Kumuwa contrary to section 501 of the Papua New Guinea Criminal Code. How do you plead: guilty or not guilty?'

One interpreter translated this into Tok Pisin and the second interpreter translated that into Melpa. Yaubriki listened and then replied without hesitation. The eventual translation into English was: 'Yes, I killed him'.

The young Australian barrister from the Public Solicitor's Office rose to his feet and, on behalf of his client, entered a plea of 'not guilty'. As this was translated, Yaubriki frowned with puzzled caution. He was probably unaware that, under the Criminal Code, a defence counsel was permitted to enter such a plea in circumstances where his client might not be familiar with the workings of Australian law. Conviction on a charge of Wilful

Murder carries a mandatory penalty of 'death by hanging unless the trial judge finds extenuating circumstances'. In fact, for many years the judges had defied the legislature and had invariably found 'extenuating circumstances' but it still meant an oppressively long period of imprisonment and defence counsel routinely challenged this by a technical plea of 'not guilty'.

As the Crown witnesses gave their evidence, the story unfolded of Yaubriki being startled to observe a neighbour – who was apparently party to some intra-village feud – make a vicious attack on his wife. He had extracted a machete from his dying wife's hand and killed the assailant. Anticipating retaliation from the kinsfolk of the man he had killed, he hiked for some miles to the nearest police patrol post and described fumblingly what had happened:[3]

> Sub-inspector Tami: You are now free – you are not under arrest. What I did to you I keep you from the sight of the people who wanted to fight with you. You are not obliged to say anything unless you wish to do so, but whatever you do say will be taken in writing and may be given in evidence. Do you wish to say anything?

> Yaubriki: Yes. I would like to talk. On Wednesday evening it was dark and I came home to Keforo village in my haus pik. There were argument between my wife and Zorike. A fight broke out between them. I knew nothing about the beginning of their argument.

> I then sat down outside near the fire and listening to them. After that Zorike held his bush knife and walked towards my wife and cut her. First he cuts my wife on her left arm, and then again under her left ear right down the neck. This time she felt down when received last cut on the neck. Zorike wanted to run away but could not do so because he received three cuts from my wife – Etamo cut him on his face right down his eyes, then

---

[3] Most of the chapters of this book recount happenings which have been shared with colleagues within an oral tradition. However, in this particular case I still have the court documents before me as I write. As usual, the police interview was passed through two interpreters and the interviewing sub-officer's translation into English is rather inept but I insist on transcribing it verbatim.

on his left shoulder. Zorike wanted to graped[4] the knife from Etamo and they pulled the knife and cut the right finger of him. My wife then felt down into the ground. When I saw my wife felt down and beginning to die Zorike wanted to run away. I then said: 'I have only one wife and now she died'. I then pulled the bush knife out of the hand of my wife and held it on my hand and ran behind Zorike and cut him as well on his left side face. When I cut him on his face he felt down onto the ground. When he was on the ground I then took the hard piece of wood of fence stick and hit him on his low back twice and third of it, I hit him on his back kneck and fourth I break his head by hitting it. I was very cross because he killed my wife already. Therefore I am thinking to kill him as well so he can die with my wife. I had been married to five wives and four of them already died and Etamo is the last wife. I also the leader of the tribes in my village during the fights between the tribes. At that time when I saw my wife died I was worrying a lots, because I am an old man and who is going to marriage me again and who is going to look after my pigs? I lost my wife now. You have seen all my pigs – I have plenty pigs.

On conclusion of evidence and addresses by counsel, the judge indicated that he would remand the prisoner in custody overnight while he considered his judgment. It was late afternoon and I stood and mumbled: 'Silence all stand. This honourable court is now adjourned until the forenoon. God save the Queen!'

It could be seen as improper for a Supreme Court judge to talk informally with the opposing barristers when a case was still in progress and so the routine was for the judge and I to share dinner at the local hotel when proceedings were adjourned for the day. As his Associate, I had an ill-defined role as something between aide-de-camp, tipstaff, body-guard, private secretary and drinking companion. He would sometimes ponder over the day's proceedings. I was not even a qualified lawyer and could certainly offer no comment but occasionally he would 'think out loud', within the privacy of the last whisky after dinner, about the things which troubled him. And that night he was clearly troubled. He rambled on about the traditions of British law – trial by one's

---

4   Presumably 'grabbed' or 'grasped'. The original Tok Pisin was *holim*.

peers, trial by ordeal and all that sort of stuff – even mentioning the archaic sentence of 'imprisonment to the rising of the court'. With my meagre training in the Sociology of Law I vaguely remembered that the latter was occasionally used by the circuit judges in feudal England. Faced by irrefutable evidence that a noble had killed someone, the king's judges of Henry the Second's day were reluctant to impose the death penalty but had to respond with some symbolic action; the prisoner would suffer the humiliation of being held in chains and paraded around the country until the judge had completed his month-long circuit throughout the counties and then released with honour being satisfied on all sides. I bought His Honour one more whisky and he retired to his hotel bedroom to write his 'judgment on sentence'.

At ten the next morning we all assembled. Yaubriki stood impassively in the dock. The judge read a carefully prepared written judgment:[5]

> The Crown alleges that on the night of the 27th of April at the village of Kefeno the accused unlawfully killed a fellow villager, Zorike Kumuwa, and that at the time of so doing he intended to cause the man's death. It is a sad case and I have reached a strong conclusion upon the evidence presented. I am satisfied as to the following matters:
>
> 1. The accused is not a young man. He is a villager governed by custom and, in emotional reactions, by his environment and the traditions of his people. I suspect he was a warrior in the past.
>
> 2. In the evening of the 27th of April the accused was sitting by a fire near his pig house. His wife Etamo and Zorike were working in or about the pig house. The witness Hinahowa Bode was nearby.
>
> 3. An argument broke out between Etamo and Zorike. Both were probably carrying bush knives. Zorike struck Etamo with his knife – a sharp, dangerous weapon. Etamo fought back and inflicted some lacerations to the face and shoulder. In the struggle Zorike also suffered lacerations to the finger. However

---

5   Again, I have the document before me as I write and I transcribe verbatim.

he inflicted injuries which resulted in Etamo's death soon after and she fell mortally wounded to the ground. The accused witnessed what was in effect the killing of his wife – his only wife upon whom he relied in his advancing years.

4. The accused's reaction was immediate. He took the knife from his dying wife's hand and struck at least one blow to Zorike's head which felled him. He then seized a stick and beat Zorike vigorously, inflicting fractures of the skull which resulted in Zorike's death soon after. I find there was no apparent period between the felling of his wife and his attack upon Zorike.

5. The accused made a full explanation of these events to Sub-inspector Tami who took a detailed statement from him (Exhibit E). I am satisfied that this represented a true account of what the accused said.

Thus, to sum up, the accused killed the man whom he had just seen killing his own wife. I have no hesitation in finding – in fact the evidence compels me to do so – that the accused, and of course his wife, had suffered a wrongful act of an extreme nature. I cannot ignore the accused's environment, customs and upbringing. I find that the killing of his wife deprived him of his self-control and induced the immediate assault upon his wife's killer. I return a verdict of not guilty on the offence charged in the indictment but I return a verdict of guilty of manslaughter.

Asking for support from the interpreters, His Honour then switched to less formal language. He explained that the court had formally decided that Yaubriki had indeed killed the deceased and that, as a judge and representative of the Law, he had no alternative but to record a conviction on manslaughter and impose a sentence of imprisonment. There was a silence and he said: 'And so I sentence you to the rising of the court'.

He paused and nodded to me: 'Mr Associate, you may now declare the sittings ended'. I was sitting at the desk just below him, pen poised to record the sentence in the record book and was momentarily flustered. It took a few seconds for me to sort out what was going on and then to rise and awkwardly say: 'These sittings of the Supreme Court of Papua New Guinea are now ended. God save the Queen!'

The judge bowed to the assembly, said: 'You may now release the prisoner', and withdrew. There was some confusion. Defence counsel, working through the interpreters, explained to Yaubriki the outcome of the judge's ruling. Yaubriki listened carefully and pondered. He straightened himself and said softly: *'Jas i bikpela man tru. I gat savi long pasin bilong tumbuna'* (The judge is an honourable man. He has the wisdom of the ancients).

He bowed to the now vacant judge's chair and left the courtroom.

10

THE SMELL OF RUM

Rum is rum. You can no more separate the smell and the taste than you can separate the soul and the body of a living person.

I developed a liking for it in Darwin where, on long bush trips, the ice packed around the beer cans melted after the first day or so and you had to fall back on spirits.

But the smell seeps through the pores of your skin. I gave up drinking it in Papua New Guinea when I moved in with Maria. I remember watching her sprawled beside me and beginning to stir as the first dapplings of daylight touched the curtains. In our steamy little Port Moresby flat the air hung heavy with the smell of the night's love-making and the lingering rum in my skin. To me, it was a living, human smell but Maria's nose twitched and she grumbled in her sleep. Later, when the Monsoon Season came in earnest, she complained that she found the smell nauseating and I readjusted my drinking habits and committed myself to drinking only beer.

It was ten years before I tasted rum again. Sergeant Ken Longman, my colleague at the Police Cadet Academy in Melbourne, mentioned over breakfast one day that one of his men was off sick and he needed another staff member to assist in taking a squad of cadets on the mandatory visit to the city morgue. I reluctantly volunteered and presented myself at the squad classroom at ten a.m.

Twenty of the kids sat behind desks giggling and chattering while waiting for their sergeant to appear. They looked skinny and awkward in their short-back-and-sides haircuts. Regulations prescribed that police uniforms were not worn on 'excursions' and they were dressed in a variety of ill-fitting suits whose colours often clashed with the shirts and ties selected by these eager seventeen-year-olds.

The squad snapped to attention as Ken strode in and commenced his briefing. He reminded them of the two week's study they had done of the *Coroners Court Act* and explained that the morning's work would consist of hearing a lecture from a Coroners Court official, spending some time in the cool rooms and, finally, observing a post mortem examination.

The period in the cool rooms, he explained, was simply a matter of familiarisation. 'It is not a particularly pleasant place,' he said. 'If you feel you must vomit, do so in the wash basin. No-one will laugh at you. You have got to get used to this: we don't want you to make a fool of yourself on the first fatal car smash you attend.'

The cadets nodded earnestly.

Ken, an aging sergeant nearing retirement, was something of a father-figure to the cadets and he muttered some gentle advice about buying spearmint lollies if they had a queasy stomach. I noted that his advice was gratuitous as many of the kids where already chomping on lollies or chewing gum. The compulsory visit to the morgue was part of the folk-lore of cadet training and the older cadets had already explained it all, in lurid, exaggerated detail, to the younger cadets who had religiously bought packets of 'Peppermint Lifesavers' and 'PK Chewing Gum'. We moved out of the squad room and into the morning sunshine of Spencer Street like a line of cud-chewing cows.

The Coroners Court was only a few hundred metres down the road. We sat on the stiff, polished pews of the empty courtroom and a jaded, leather-faced public servant gave a half-hour briefing on the paperwork required under the Regulations to the *Coroners Court Act*; Schedule A; Schedule C(ii); Form 467; Notification to the Public Trustee. A mass of typing is involved in consigning the husk of a once-breathing human being to the refrigerated vaults of the city morgue.

Eventually we moved down to the back of the building and were ushered into the refrigeration rooms. The harsh fluorescent light accentuated the glistening coldness of the aluminium trolleys cluttered, side by side, around the walls. Each held a naked husk.

To the left of the entrance door a withered old lady lay in a foetal position, one arm upraised as if to ward off something. Presumably rigor mortis had set in long before she had been found and brought here and she perched precariously on the trolley like a stick insect on a biologist's microscope slide. Beside her, on the next trolley, a plump, middle-aged gentleman sprawled on his back with the peace of one of those granite figures you find reclining on medieval tombstones in English cathedrals. His registration number and date of admission was scrawled, in felt-tip pen, across his bare thigh. His left ankle was touched by the shrivelled claw of the occupant of the next trolley: an apparently young man whose facial features had been obliterated in a traffic collision.

The air in the room was an icy combination of decay and disinfectant. You could not separate the two.

'Relax and get used to it', boomed the morgue attendant in white boiler-suit and gumboots. 'Don't be afraid to touch.'

Cadet O'Callaghan, ever anxious to please, grinned sheepishly and patted a frigid set of grey buttocks.

The gentleman in gumboots opened the door to the 'deep freeze' room which accommodated the badly decomposed bodies. The cadets were ushered in one by one. It was a dark cavern of shrivelled bodies and crumbly stuff in plastic coffin bags and you could only glance at the scene briefly and then withdraw from the choking smell.

We returned to the main cool room and wandered among the trolleys. As a civilian instructor in Sociology at the Academy I had an ambiguous role. I was expected to be something between an academic and a scoutmaster to 'the lads', as the older police staff members insisted on calling the cadets. One supported and guided the kids as best one could and tried to provide a responsible 'stiff upper lip' example which would help them through their future careers. But, at that moment, I badly needed to vomit. I had sunk a few beers the night before and could feel the phlegm from god-knows-how-many cigarettes grumbling insistently at my gut. Cadet O'Callaghan asked me about the legal implications of the fact that the corpse on the fourth trolley to the right appeared to have grossly mutilated genitals. I tersely told him that we would discuss it in the class the next morning, not now.

Ken assembled the cadets in the corridor and explained that members of the Detective Training School were observing the post mortem in the operating theatre behind the cool rooms and that we would have to wait our turn. We shuffled around the ante room for half-an-hour until Ken instructed the squad to return to the Academy and prepare for the afternoon classes.

I was seated outside the post mortem room, smoking a cigarette and trying to pretend that I was not conscious of the metallic shriek of the little circular saw used by the attendants to remove the tops of skulls in readiness for the medico to lift out the brains. The saw had a high-pitched whine.

'Thanks for your assistance', said Ken, touching my shoulder. 'It's a pity that we can't let the lads see a proper post mortem. It's after twelve and I had to send them back to the Academy for the afternoon lectures. But look, this PM will be finished in another five minutes and the Detective Training School mob will leave; you and I could stay on and check out the next one. It sounds interesting: an arson case.'

I lied. Lied like a pig in shit. 'Ken that's good of you. I'd like to stay but I've got a heap of exam papers to correct back at the Academy. I'll have to leave now.'

After the chill air-conditioning of the Coroners Court building, the noisy bustle of Flinders Street hit like a monsoon storm – hot, turbulent and enveloping, but unsettling. I wandered down the street.

The public bar of 'Markillies' pub caters for an odd assortment of wharfies from the night shift, painters and dockers and the sad old alcoholics, who wait anxiously for its doors to open early in the morning. It was years since I had been there and the atmosphere hadn't changed. Gratefully I sank onto a bar stool and ordered a pot of beer.

The gentleman on the adjoining bar stool was in his sixties and dressed in a greasy gaberdine overcoat. 'Had a rough day, son?' he inquired.

'No, mate, just another day – another day, another dollar.'

He nodded sympathetically.

I sniffed my beer but could detect nothing of the familiar aroma. My clothes and skin were permeated by that inseparable combination of decomposition and disinfectant. I went to the toilet and washed my hands and face under the tap. It made no difference.

I glanced uneasily at the gentleman in the gaberdine coat. I could catch a trace of his scent – a combination of stale tobacco smoke and sweat – and wondered if he was conscious of my pervasive aura of death. I edged the bar stool a little to the left to increase the gap between us.

The barmaid noted my empty glass. 'Another beer, love?'

'No, love. Thanks, but I can't seem to get the taste of it today.'

'Well then, a rum?'

I paused and nodded appreciatively.

The first one hit the back of my throat but was relatively tasteless.

The second one stirred a few old memories of Port Moresby. Momentarily I could recall a night when Maria and I had slept on the verandah during a rainstorm.

The third one had the taste/smell of rum. The clinging cloud of disinfectant began to disperse.

I didn't feel like eating that night and went to bed early. Somewhere around midnight Maria slipped in beside me and curled into my arms.

Her nose twitched and she uncurled. 'You've been drinking rum again. Christ you disgust me! Haven't you got any sense of smell?'

11

CONSTABLE

Five months as a rookie at the Academy. Twelve months as a probationary constable at the training station. One month of lectures and exams back at headquarters. And he had made it. The Police Gazette confirmed his appointment as a General Duties Constable.

He checked his watch for the third time. Ten-forty. About right for the night shift: any earlier and he might appear over-eager, any later and he might appear slack. He flicked away the cigarette and moved towards the lights of the station, unconsciously running a finger down the crease of the crisp uniform shirt. It had come back from the laundry neatly packed in polythene but he had found himself touching up the creases with an iron during a restless afternoon of waiting for his first shift.

'You must be the new bloke. Jesus, it's a bit rough giving you a night shift on your first day here. A cunt of a night too. My name's Charlie. The mess room is down there. Make me a cup of coffee while you are at it. Black, two sugars.' It all tumbled out cheerfully without any pause for breath between sentences. He was about twenty, sandy-haired and chunky.

Len mumbled his name and leaned awkwardly over the counter. He shook the young constable's hand and then headed down the corridor.

The mess room was almost identical to that of his old training station. The Laminex-covered table with the crusted tomato sauce bottle, the bare walls painted in institutional cream gloss, the noticeboard cluttered with departmental memos, newspaper clippings and faded photocopies of pornographic cartoons. He made two cups of coffee from the electric urn and carried them back to the front counter knowing that, at ten forty-five p.m., Charlie would be the only man in the building and unable to leave the switchboard until the afternoon shift crews returned to the station.

Len sat on the desk beside the switchboard, lit a cigarette and chatted. Charlie was younger than him but, within the pecking order of the staff of a suburban station, considerably senior by virtue of his couple of months there as a constable and Len was grateful for his inside information, delivered with unmalicious sarcasm, on who was who in the sub-district.

'I don't know whether the senior sergeant is crooked on you or something but he has rostered you on the station car this week with Turtle Ferguson. Jesus!'

'Turtle is a lazy cunt', he added by way of explanation.

Conversation was interrupted by the divisional van and the station car pulling up outside almost simultaneously as the afternoon shift crews prepared to knock off. A Traffic Operations Group car with a two-man crew on the same shift pulled in a few minutes later. This was followed by a Dog Squad panel van driven by a senior constable who was on the six-to-two shift but who knew that eleven p.m. – shift change-over – was the most convivial time for a tea break at the nearest station. Suddenly the room was crowded with men shedding overcoats, checking in equipment and trading gossip noisily. Len shook hands all round and shyly asked questions.

They all drifted down to the mess room and a pot of tea was brewed. At about eleven-fifteen the loud conversation ebbed briefly as a middle-aged senior constable strode through towards the locker room with an incoherent grunt of greeting. 'That's Turtle', Charlie whispered. 'Have a happy evening!'

By eleven-thirty the night shift crew on the divie van were out on the road, most of the afternoon shift had gone home and Len sat silently at the mess room table with Charlie and the Dog Squad bloke, who was drinking his third cup of tea. Turtle appeared around the locker room door, protruding only his head and shoulders. 'You're the new kid? OK. Get the car around to the back and we'll head off.'

Charlie organised Len, getting the ignition keys, checking out a revolver to him, supplying a clipboard with fresh running sheets and introducing him to the night-shift constable manning the switchboard. He winked and repeated 'Have a happy evening!'

Len drove the car around to the back of the station and watched Turtle load a pillow and two blankets into the back seat with a gruff, guilty glance towards him.

Len eased the car into the light traffic moving south in High Street. The radio babbled constantly as usual. He was well trained in the routine of notifying VKC when the car is back on patrol, but had never been in the position of both driving and handling the radio. He peered into the rear vision mirror which revealed Turtle slumped silently in the back seat. With another hesitant glance at the mirror – the senior constable was awake but watching the traffic with a bored, unfocussed gaze – he fumbled for the microphone.

VKC, this is Northcote TWO-HUNDRED.

Northcote TWO-HUNDRED?

Clearing the station. Two up. We're in High Street moving south.

Roger TWO-HUNDRED.

They had a couple of traffic matters, none of them involving arrests.

At about eleven-thirty there was the usual 'rowdy youths' call from VKC: a bunch of kids leaving a party in Clark Street and breaking branches off trees in the newly planted nature strip. Len felt slightly anxious as he swung the car in beside them and flicked on the revolving blue light. 'Psychological warfare', he thought to himself. 'It doesn't achieve anything specific but it creates the impression that we mean business.'

Then he relaxed as he realised they really were kids: none of them more than about fifteen. Half of them were giggling little tarts with black eye-shadow applied in quantities aimed at compensating for the barely pubescent tits which poked against garish tee-shirts.

Turtle lumbered out of the car. Len, holding a torch, stood on the footpath facing a semi-circle of nervous kids. Turtle said nothing. Self-consciously Len gave the usual lecture about what would happen to them if they didn't get home immediately and the kids dispersed.

Turtle returned to the back seat without a word and pulled the blanket over himself. Len sat behind the steering wheel and made the usual entry into the running sheet and the usual call back to VKC, his voice sounding oddly loud in the silence of the stationary car. With a twinge of anger he slammed the car into first gear and headed back towards High Street.

Turtle did not even get out of the car on the next job. It was a small sedan going through a stop light in Station Street with a brashness which obliged Len to switch on the blue light and pull it over. The driver turned out to be a young, blond school-teacher who smiled weakly and did the 'scatter-brained-female bit'. Len wrote out a Traffic Infringement Notice. Expertly he assessed that her breath might bring her pretty close to the 0.08% blood/alcohol concentration but, with another twinge of anger at the lack of support from his senior constable, he curtly handed over the T.I.N. and wished her goodnight without going back to the car to get the Preliminary Breath Test kit. She drove off at a repentant fifty kilometres per hour.

Northcote TWO-HUNDRED?

It was getting on to three a.m. Len was tired – half-conscious of a certain impotent anger – and he took longer than usual to reach for the microphone and reply.

VKC, this is Northcote TWO-HUNDRED.

> *TWO-HUNDRED, a domestic in Claude Street – can you handle it?*

Two-hundred. OK.

> *Roger, TWO-HUNDRED. It's at THREE SEVEN ZERO Claude –*

*CHARLIE-LIMA-ALPHA-UNIFORM-
DELTA-ECHO. Complainant won't
give her name but says that she
lives at that address and has been
assaulted by her husband.*

Roger, VKC.

*Roger, that job to you at ZERO
TWO FOUR SIX.*

Len did a right turn at the next intersection and headed east
at a steady sixty-five kilometres per hour. No need for lights and
siren on an ordinary domestic.

*VKC, this is Northcote THREE-
HUNDRED.*

Northcote THREE-HUNDRED?

*Reference your last on a domestic
at Claude Street for Northcote
TWO-HUNDRED. Could you inform
the crew that we know that
address well – this has been the
third call on night shift in the last
week – they're a middle-aged
couple – both alcoholics – he beats
the hell out of her – a no-joy job.
It's a brick flat with a plum tree in
the front garden. We are just
north of Darebin and High and
are clear to provide back-up if you
want.*

*Roger, THREE-HUNDRED, will
relay your info. Northcote TWO-
HUNDRED did you catch that
transmission from the van?*

*TWO-HUNDRED. Yes, VKC, I got
it.*

Gratuitously, Len added :

Thanks, mate.

As they turned into Claude Street he raised his head awkwardly to check, through the rear vision mirror, whether Turtle was awake. Their eyes met. He was sprawled underneath the blanket, head on the pillow with his eyes open. 'Yeah, I know the address too, son. A pair of fuckwits. I wish he'd kill the silly bitch and she'd stop bothering us. You handle it. It's just a domestic.'

With what could have been a trace of apology, he added: 'I've had a bastard of a day', and rolled over and closed his eyes.

All the lights seemed to be on in the flat. Len knocked, transferred the torch to his left hand and moved to one side of the door as he had been trained to do at the Academy.

'Christ, it took you long enough to get here!' she shrilled before she had the door fully open. She was dressed in a rumpled dressing gown and had a trickle of blood running from a gash on the temple somewhere beneath the edge of her hair.

He moved cautiously into the bare, drab lounge-room. A thick-set man in his late forties or early fifties, clutching a can of beer, was sprawled in an arm chair in front of the television set which flickered out a black-and-white movie.

He turned his head lazily towards Len. 'Well, the fucking forces of law and order arrive in strength, eh?'

'You shut up', she shrieked. 'He's only doing his job. He's going to lock you up, you pig, for what you did to me! And locking up is too good for a filthy pig like you – you deserve better – you should be castrated!'

'And you know what you deserve, you fucking moll!' he roared, looming up from the chair and knocking her back against the wall with a sweeping backhander.

Len took two clumsy steps backward. His hand dithered between the baton in his right-hand pocket and the revolver strapped cross-draw on the left of his belt, and then slacked helplessly to his side with the realisation that neither was appropriate.

She sagged against the wall, sobbing.

The husband turned slowly – ominously slowly – towards Len.

'And now you can fuck off back to kindergarten, kiddie cop!' He said it with a quiet deliberation which gave no warning of the long, sweeping right-cross he aimed at Len's head.

He was fairly drunk and Len was fairly fit. Len instinctively ducked below the sweeping fist and found himself in that position which is every boxer's dream: a jutting jaw and a lumbering, off-balance opponent. He put all the force he could muster into one savage uppercut and the husband sank to his knees, eyes closed and head moving dumbly from side to side in an unconscious attempt to shake off the blood which spurted from his lips.

She fell around her husband. 'You pig! You copper cunt!' she screamed, 'You've hurt him! You had no right to do that!'

As Len let himself out the front door she was shrieking something about police brutality.

He sank into the front seat of the car. Without glancing at the sleeping senior constable in the back seat, he reached for the microphone and gave the usual call to cancel back-up. He lit a cigarette and made the usual entry in the running sheet: 'Domestic at 370 Claude Street. No offence disclosed. Civil action advised' and started the car with weary, deliberate movements.

12

THIS-FELLER

Jack moves slowly. Even when they were in the heat of mustering he would move slowly. The young stockmen have no sense of how scrub cattle instinctively react: a breakaway from the gathering herd and the young blokes substitute rapid action for judgment and make it worse. You need to know the moods of the cattle and the country. And it takes forty years or more to know the gullies, plains and waterholes of Cameron River Downs Station.

Jack was the Head Stockman because of just such a forty years of gazing, listening and moving slowly. He had never left Cameron River Downs but someone once told him that in some of the other big stations the Head Stockman had his living quarters with the white jackeroos or even in the homestead paddock. Jack was content with the Aboriginal stockmen's camp by the dry creek bed. It was his own natural home where he was lord. He was not in fact full-blood – about three-quarter caste – but his numerous children were never taunted by the others for the trace of lightness in their skin: their father was 'Jack the Head Stockman' whose authority and wisdom were beyond question. His wife was full-blood and chattered to the other women in Bamyili dialect. Jack had been raised at Ernabella Mission and spoke little of her language. But it was of no consequence as he spoke little anyway.

Towards the end of the dry season he was checking the northern stock camps. He halted on a slight rise and sat in silence for a long time, body swaying in unconscious adjustment to the movements of the fidgeting horse. He gazed. The plain sprawled. The universe revolved timelessly around the axis of Cameron River Downs Station.

Unbeknown to Jack, the station was also the axis of a conference taking place in an air-conditioned office in Darwin, three hundred miles to the north. The Director of the Department of Health riffled through a pile of papers stacked at the head of the polished conference table which was flanked by the Assistant Director (Preventive Medicine), the Assistant Director (Contagious Diseases), the Assistant Director (Prosecutions) and the new Community Health expert. A representative of the Police and the Welfare Branch attended as there were likely to be charges laid under the *Infectious Diseases Act*.

The Director outlined the situation tersely. Routine reports had suggested an alarming incidence of venereal disease in the area of Cameron River Downs Station. Discreet inquiries had revealed that the departmental nursing sister, responsible for one of the usual caravan-based medical clinics allocated to the large cattle stations, had been providing certain services to lonely stockmen.

It had, the Director explained, the makings of a political scandal if the press got wind of it and the Minister for Health had personally demanded action of him. The sister had, of course, been dismissed but an epidemiological problem remained. Cameron River Downs Station sprawls over an area of desolate bushland roughly the size of Belgium, its only centre being the cluster of buildings in the dusty compound by the homestead: the fuel depot, the pay office, the general store, the Health Department caravan and the Education Department mobile school. Men from the outer stock camps came in, picked up their pay – and god knows what else – and returned. They are a breed of men not noted for chastity and the huge, isolated station had become a medical disaster zone within which the gonorrhoea bacterium was multiplying exponentially. The root of the problem – one nursing sister with a dose and a bank balance which now matched her libidinal drive – had been eliminated but the situation called for an exhaustive survey of all adults in the area to ensure that the epidemic could be charted and controlled.

Nick, seated at the lower end of the conference table, raised his hand. Like a school teacher, the Director nodded permission to speak. Nick was the idealistic young doctor appointed to the newly created 'community health' position. He had a dubious record of work in some community clinic in a working-class suburb of Melbourne and there were rumours of involvement in the leftist Doctors' Reform Society. But even the jaded officials of the Northern Territory Health Department found it hard to dislike the open-faced newcomer whose enthusiasm bubbled patently and harmlessly.

Nick proposed a month-long programme whereby he would head a team of two sisters and a medical technician who would set up a base on the station and do a systematic check of the populace – ostensibly for research purposes. The community would not be alarmed and they could treat first-phase cases on the spot, arrange treatment in Darwin for severe cases, plot the tangled lines of transmission and eventually develop a community awareness programme to forestall further outbreaks.

The Director was uneasy with this 'community awareness' stuff but he was conscious of the pressure from his Minister and desperate to pass the responsibility on to someone else. He muttered some misgivings and authorised expenditure for the project.

Nick was ready to move within two days. The flight down from Darwin intrigued him. He had travelled extensively in Europe and India but had never been confronted by the silent grandeur of these withered, limitless plains. The landing strip at Cameron River Downs Station was red, sandy dust.

He ritually discussed problems with the station manager, organised acceptable accommodation for his medical team and established a rough clinic in the aluminium caravan deserted by the disgraced sister.

He knew community health work well and prudently allocated two days of inaction to simply attune himself to the local scene. By the end of the second day he knew where he had to begin within the hierarchy of the station staff.

'Good morning, Jack. I believe you're the Head Stockman. My name is Nick. I'm a doctor. It's good of you to give me some of your time.' He gestured towards a chair in the cramped caravan.

Jack stood, a little puzzled. One stands while talking about serious matters with one's peers and, although the white bloke was young, the station manager had said that he was an important official. He shuffled uneasily but did not sit.

Nick nodded acceptance.

'Jack,' he said, 'I'm a doctor but I didn't ask to see you because you're sick. I want to see all the people on the station and the obvious place to start is with the Head Stockman. It's a survey.'

Jack turned the word 'survey' over in his mind. It meant nothing but it had a nice sound to it. Round and smooth with a gentle lilt. 'Survey ... survey.' The heeler bitch was ready to whelp; if there was a good male pup needing a name, he might use that. 'Way back, Survey, get around 'em, boy!' A good name.

'The Health Department in Darwin sent me', the doctor said.

Jack pondered. He had a fairly sketchy notion of where Darwin was but did know that it was a long way away and so the visit must be an important one.

'And for a start, I'd like to examine you.'

'Examine?'

Nick frowned in self-deprecation. He should, he realised, be using terms familiar to the patient. Consciously he adjusted his language. 'If you don't mind, Jack, I'd like to look at your cock.'

'This-feller?' Jack gestured towards an area below his huge belly sagging over a stockman's belt.

Nick nodded professionally.

Jack moved slowly. The white doctor was strange but, for a young bloke, he had a certain courtesy which you could not deny. Jack unbuttoned his jeans and laid out a large, flaccid penis. He held it with pride. 'Proper big-feller, this one, Boss.'

Nick grunted agreement, checked it for chancres and squeezed the tip gently for tell-tale pus.

'Boss, you're a doctor: you reckon there's something wrong with this-feller?'

'No, no, Jack, not at all. I just wanted to have a look at it.'

Jack tucked it back into his jeans and stood in thought for some minutes. Then he reassured the young bloke. 'Don't you worry, Boss,' he said, 'anytime you want to fly all the way down from Darwin to have a look at this-feller, that's all right by me.

13

THE PARTY

'You're not really a policeman, are you?'

He nodded shyly. She wore stylishly groomed hair and too much perfume.

The music stopped.

'You dance well. It's hard to imagine you with a baton and a row of shiny buttons.'

He explained that he was a senior constable in a Crime Car Squad and worked in plain clothes. Ineptly he tried to make a wry comment about not normally taking his baton to parties but it came out awkwardly – sounding sarcastic, even arrogant.

'Am I being too personal?' she said.

He floundered. 'Well, as a matter of fact. . .' and then tailed off, realising that he was making it even worse.

She shrugged and released his hand. Petulantly she turned and merged back into the crowd, searching for the Bacardi and Coke which she had left on a sideboard.

He returned to the table, sank down opposite Simon with a muttered apology and tried to pick up the threads of their conversation. He was annoyed at his own ineptness but also irritated by her intrusion. She was apparently the new Drama teacher at Sandra's school and had appeared abruptly with a slightly drunken demand that he dance with her. In other circumstances that would be fine, even flattering – god knows, he was a balding male in his forties and she was a rather glamorous young lady – but she had seemed blandly insensitive to the fact that he and Simon were deep in conversation.

Simon, however, seemed unconcerned. He refilled their glasses and continued with what he was saying.

Dave was normally uneasy at these end-of-school-year parties thrown by Sandra's colleagues. A childless couple in their forties – he a policeman and she a primary school teacher – somehow seemed out of place, but Sandra always insisted that they go.

But tonight had been good. It was a sprawling old weather-board house in Clifton Hill, tatty but comfortable. A number of Sandra's work mates whom he had come to know were there and he had found himself relaxing into the atmosphere of the large, lazily untidy loungeroom filled with people dancing, chatting and arguing amiably.

He especially liked Sandra's friend Susan: a gentle but intense Filipino-Chinese girl who taught Migrant English at the school. She had a reserved grace yet a glowing sexuality which intrigued him because the combination of the two fitted none of the stereotypes pushed by the Australian media as to what constitutes a 'beautiful woman'. She often came home with Sandra for a cup of coffee at the end of the school day and, if Dave were home, off-duty until the eleven p.m. commencement of night shift, he would join them, listening happily to their gossip of the day's work.

Tonight, she was accompanied by her Australian-born husband, Simon. Dave had never met him but instinctively liked him. He was a marine biologist – bearded, sombre and awkwardly polite. When they were introduced Dave sensed that he also felt a little out of place amid the clattering shop-talk of a group of teachers and they had opened a bottle of beer and settled themselves at a corner of the large table in the loungeroom.

He explained that he was working on pollution control for a paper manufacturing company. Dave expressed interest and Simon talked at length about the ecological problems of disposing of industrial waste into the waterways or the sea. At one point he paused and inquired how Dave earned a living. Dave replied. Simon nodded and continued.

Dave relaxed and went to the fridge for another bottle of beer. As he threaded his way back through the dancing couples it occurred to him that Simon would probably have reacted no differently if he had said 'used car salesman', 'bookie' or 'brain surgeon'. Simon appeared to be engrossed in his work and happy to talk about it with anyone, unconcerned with tensions of the status or class of the person he was sharing a drink with.

Dave refilled their glasses and asked about the news in the press of an epidemic of the crown of thorns starfish on the Great Barrier Reef. He had never been out of Victoria but had done a bit of scuba diving in Port Phillip Bay and he was fascinated by Simon's description of the shifting interaction of the various forms of marine life on a coral reef. They talked avidly.

Somewhere around eleven Dave was describing the sensation of diving at about six metres and finding himself in the centre of a flickering swirl of a school of fish feeding off a reef. Simon related a similar experience while snorkelling off the northern Queensland coast and they argued with animation about the changing effects of colours some six metres down.

The Drama teacher reappeared. She was somewhat tipsy and settled herself between them with determination. Tacitly both men accepted that the discussion would have to be postponed to another day and Simon politely rose and got her another drink. She talked about her experience of transferring from a New South Wales school to the one where Sandra worked. She obviously admired Sandra's competence and seemed to enjoy working at the new school.

By midnight, however, the conversation drifted in the inevitable direction. It seemed, Dave thought to himself, that whenever he met strangers who had discovered that he was a policeman, he ended up being regaled with stories either about policemen who had been particularly nasty or policemen who had been particularly nice. The former category of anecdote he could cope with: he had been in The Job for twenty years and had few illusions about its sordid reality. It was the second category of anecdotes which generally hurt: their implied message was that, contrary to all reliable sources, some policemen really are human.

She opted for the former category. It was a boring story about some constable pulling her car over and delivering a male chauvinist lecture about the stupidity of women drivers. Dave nodded sympathetically and said that it was unfortunately not uncommon.

She moved into higher gear. 'Would you agree,' she demanded, 'that the Victorian Police have a worse record of brutality than the New South Wales police?' He mumbled something about never having had any real contact with the New South Wales force and, in any case, he was hardly an objective judge as he had a natural loyalty to the Victoria Police.

Eventually it all tumbled out – the story she really wanted to tell. It concerned a political demonstration earlier that year. She had been on the periphery and uninvolved but had observed the violence of it all. Dave murmured something about demonstrations being the most unpleasant contact between police and the public, with inevitable loss of dignity on both sides. He rose, went to the sideboard and refilled her Bacardi and Coke.

She accepted the glass aggressively, drained half of it and launched into a bitterly colourful description of the sadism and brutality she had observed. Dave opened another beer and listened impassively. He had not been involved in that particular bun fight but had vague memories of mess room gossip about it: it had been handled, as far as he could recall, by Independent Patrol Group with back-up from the City Traffic boys plus any available connies from City West and had been a run-of-the-mill no-joy job.

In graphic, and sometimes noisy, detail she described how a young constable had gleefully kicked a demonstrator into unconsciousness. Dave nodded stoically. Silently he pondered how the hypothetical constable could achieve such a feat while maintaining invisibility from his Sector Sergeant, the ever-present police photographers and, presumably, the cameras of television news teams . . . but he let it pass.

'And you were one of them?'

He shook his head slowly and explained that he had been on afternoon-shift patrol and had only second-hand knowledge of the incident.

'So you missed the opportunity to get stuck into the students with your baton?'

It was a mindless, rhetorical question to which there was no reply and he could do nothing but take another sip of beer.

'They love it, you know! All of them had removed the metal numbers from their shirts so that they could belt the kids without fear of being identified!'

He thought steadily for a few seconds. He hated these meaningless arguments but had little alternative but to reply. He glanced apologetically at Simon and explained to her that members of the Victoria Police are not issued with the numbered metal badges worn in New South Wales.

The realisation that she had made a fool of herself hit her like a slap in the face. She paused speechless for a fraction of a second and then blustered aggressively. 'That's what I mean! You don't want to be held accountable for your thuggery. You hide behind an impersonal blue uniform!'

He hunched his shoulders and peered into his beer with resignation. Simultaneously he became conscious that most conversation in the room had halted: she was almost shouting and eyes were turned upon them. Simon shifted uneasily in his seat.

'You're all so damned smug!' she sneered, 'You set yourself up as judges of right and wrong but if an intelligent citizen confronts you with the reality of police brutality you just ignore her and drink your fucking beer, knowing that you can get away with it!'

Fortuitously the record player had reached the end of a disc and the room was in silence. Dave sensed that everyone was watching and waiting to see how he would respond. There was nothing he could do or say. Mutely he refilled his glass.

Sandra flitted across to the table and whispered something about it being time they went home. Unable to suggest an alternative, he rose, mumbled an apology to Simon, and followed her.

At the door they thanked the hostess briefly.

They drove in silence. After about five minutes, Sandra blurted out: 'Oh, Christ, why does it always happen? Why can't we ever just enjoy an ordinary party together?'

'You talk as if it was my fault.'

'No, no.'

'But there is some silly drunken bitch who disrupts a party and it is not her who has to leave – it's me. Why? Why me?'

'No, Dave, I'm not saying it is your fault . . . it's nothing you did . . . it's just . . . well, just that you're a policeman and people feel. . .'

He snapped savagely. 'And you're beginning to wish you had married a human being instead of a copper?'

'Oh, Christ!' she whispered and began to cry softly.

As usual, there was nothing he could say. They reached home in silence.

She went to bed alone. He sat at the living-room table with the overhead light off and, by the glow from the dial of the FM radio, opened a bottle of Scotch.

He woke at midday with no recollection of going to bed. She had gone to work. The radio was still burbling. The bottle of Scotch had a couple of inches left in it. The afternoon shift would commence at three. . .

14

ARSON OF A DWELLING-PLACE AT NIGHT

Penguan was a handsome woman – robust and sleek – who addressed the judge, through an interpreter, with a combination of dignified determination and the softly spoken deference of a Papua New Guinean wife.

She wore the regulation blue-and-white striped *laplap* of a remand prisoner, topped with the absurd 'Mary blouse' which was a hangover from the days of Christian missionary rule: a coy, white blouse with puffed short-sleeves which attempted, unsuccessfully, to conceal the swell of her strong breasts.

I, too, felt that my clothes were a little absurd. An associate to a judge of the Supreme Court of Papua New Guinea wears a flowing, black barristers gown, long trousers (the sweat runs down the back of your knees during the Monsoon Season) and heavily starched white shirt. After twelve months of beginning each sitting of the Supreme Court with the ritual of clipping on the 'barristers bibs' – the two strips of white cloth which hang from the collar, worn by preachers in nineteenth century Britain – I was becoming dumbly aware that I had, more or less accidentally, fallen into the role of a member of a Gilbert and Sullivan cast playing out the tragi-comedy of the dying days of Australia's colonial exploitation of Papua New Guinea. It was 1973 – two years before Independence.

She wore the *laplap* and Mary blouse with simplicity.

I had read the case file on the plane coming down from Moresby the day before. Her husband's statement, typed in English by a sergeant of the Royal Papua New Guinea Constabulary, described the circumstances of the alleged offence with a clarity which I could never surpass and I took a copy of it:

'My wives and I sleep in the same house. One of them sleeps in one room, the other in another room, and myself in another room. My second wife was menstruating and, as is our tradition, was required to sleep outside in the jungle. At about midnight the second wife returned to the house and saw that I was sleeping with my first wife in the same bed. She said to my first wife and to myself that we had arranged to sleep in separate rooms. She asked us why we were breaking this arrangement by sleeping together. My first wife became angry and began to insult my second wife who was also insulting her. I told them to be quiet because it was night and time for sleeping. My second wife ran outside and set fire to the house. I tried to stop the fire but only burnt my hands. The house burnt down. I took my second wife to the Patrol Officer at Kompian Patrol Post, thinking that he would reprimand her in the Local Court. The possessions I lost in the fire are my own personal worry and the house has been rebuilt by the village people. I have no wish to take my wife to the Big Court. That is all.'

But she was, in fact, required to appear at 'the Big Court' and I watched her give her evidence some three months later. I took it down in shorthand but could only record the stilted English of the court interpreter and not the husky sonority of her Wabag dialect:

'I returned to the house. On my arrival I saw them both sleeping together and so I scolded them and said: "We sleep separately – why do you both sleep together now?" And then the other woman scolded me and said: "We have had intercourse together . . . do you want to eat it? . . . is that why you have come back?" She said this three times. I replied: "You can eat it!" As she gave me this talk I became angry and so I set fire to the house and then went to sleep at Marim village and came to Kompian Station the next morning. That is all'.

It was not hard to imagine her nostrils flaring at the taunts from the older Number One wife. The Western Highlanders, unlike some of the coastal people, have a horror of oral-genital contact. The phrase 'You can eat it!' was the inept attempt of the interpreter to render a complex Wabag-dialect insult which could be better translated as: 'So why don't you lick up the vaginal juices and semen?' About the most savage sneer you could hurl at anyone in the Western Highlands.

Nor was it hard to imagine the aged husband muttering into his beard and pondering how best to handle all this nonsense. Number Two wife had petulantly hurled a smouldering stick from the outside campfire into the palm-leaf wall. Certainly the neighbours had rebuilt the thatched hut the next day, but such behaviour was, after all, 'not on' for a young, newly-purchased Number Two wife. He decided to maintain dignity by referring the whole matter to the *kiap* – the white-skinned government official who commanded the nearest patrol post. A reprimand was deserved.

The kiap, eager and fresh from his training period at the School of Pacific Administration in Sydney, had thumbed through the index of the large volume stamped: 'Papua New Guinea Criminal Code'. 'A' for 'aggravated rape', 'A' for 'assault', 'A' for 'attack' . . . and eventually found the appropriate section: 'A' for 'arson of a dwelling place at night'. The Papua New Guinean Criminal Code reproduces, with a few trivial changes, the Queensland Criminal Code; that, in turn, is a codification of English Common Law in relation to major offences plus odds and ends of Australian legislation in relation to minor matters. Historically, its definition of serious crimes largely arises from cases before the courts of England during the Industrial Revolution of the eighteenth and nineteenth centuries. In the crowded slums of eighteenth century London, arson of a dwelling place at night was indeed tantamount to attempted murder. A deliberately lit fire in the cluttering wooden houses, lacking reticulated water or the services of a fire brigade, could be expected to result in multiple deaths. It carries a maximum penalty of life imprisonment.

The *kiap* had little interest in British history but he did have a solid training in following written directives. The penalty specified in the Criminal Code made patent the severity of the offence.

Wabag-speaking constables were instructed to take statements, a Preliminary Hearing of the Magistrates Court was convened on the spot and Penguan was committed for trial. The paperwork was forwarded to Port Moresby where the eager young solicitors of the Law Department studied the police statements, checked the appropriate sections of the Criminal Code and agreed, after several legal conferences, that this was clearly ground for an Indictment before the Supreme Court.

The legislation has provisions for bail while awaiting trial but they are rather meaningless to an aged villager who supports his two wives and numerous children from a few coffee trees and half-an-acre of sweet potato. Penguan spent three months tending the gardens of the patrol post, dressed in her remand prisoner's *laplap* and sleeping in the tiny *calaboose* with its cordon of barbed wire.

*   *   *   *

After all the evidence had been given, the judge pronounced a verdict of 'guilty' and remanded the prisoner for sentence the next morning.

He said little to me over drinks at the end of the day's sitting. I felt for the old man: he was a good judge who struggled hard to adapt his deep training in the British legal tradition to the realities of Papua New Guinea. He sank a couple of rums and retired to his room to prepare his 'judgment on sentence'. I had some conception of his dilemma. A fine? But how the hell do you calculate the cost to the community of the loss of one thatched hut which was rebuilt the next day? A good behaviour bond? But all those bustling little bureaucrats in Moresby's Law Department, dealing with an offence under the archaic Criminal Code which carried a penalty of life imprisonment, would certainly lodge a Crown appeal against 'excessive leniency'. A compromise was his only option. I, too, sank a rum and retired.

*   *   *   *

'Prisoner at the bar, you have been found guilty of arson of a dwelling place at night. Do you have anything to say before sentence is passed upon you by this honourable court?'

'All my talk has been given to the court.'

She was sentenced to four months with hard labour.

The husband frowned as the interpreter translated it to him, muttering questions in Wabag dialect. He had, after all, spent some twenty years accruing enough pigs and land to afford the luxury of paying the 'bride price' for a second young wife with broad, attractive, potentially child-bearing hips. He had not been able to enjoy her for three months and was now faced with a further four months with only the near-toothless Number One wife. But, in his own eyes, he had acted as a *gentleman*. He nodded approvingly at the judge.

Penguan listened to the interpreter's translation. She did not nod acceptance: she gazed steadily at the judge's lips as he pronounced sentence. She turned with dignity to the constable who escorted her from the courthouse and back to the prison compound.

15

CORDON AND SEARCH

The staff of the sub-officers' course pride themselves on the weekly outdoor training exercises – meticulously prepared and thoroughly realistic.

They excelled themselves with the 'cordon and search' operation in the tiny Forestry Reserve north of Melbourne. The background briefing described how two hardened offenders had perpetrated an armed hold-up of the local bank, had panicked and taken the bank manager's daughter as hostage and had escaped by fleeing up the one-way track to the Forestry Commission's flora and fauna sanctuary.

It was the perfect setting for an exercise: only one road led to it and tourists were hardly likely to be there on a late-Autumn Wednesday morning. The forty newly promoted sergeants, undergoing the mandatory two-month course for sub-officers, were, for the purpose of the exercise, stripped of their rank and allocated to various jobs: 'inspector' responsible for the overall coordination of the operation, 'sergeant' responsible for a section of five 'constables', and so on. The two 'offenders' were eager young police cadets dressed in civilian clothing and equipped with two-way radios which allowed the training staff director of the exercise to control their movement over the thirty or forty acres of the Forestry Reserve. The 'hostage' was a plaster shop-window model, half her nose missing as a result of rough storage in the Equipment Cupboard at headquarters; she would, if all went well, be found in a shallow grave beside a bush track.

For realism, it was important that at least some of the support units of the Police Force were involved. As it happened, word of the careful planning of these exercises had spread and the commanders of a number of specialised units were keen to use them as training for their own newly recruited staff. Elements of the Communication Section, Dog Squad, Transport Section, Independent Patrol Group and others attended. Nearly one hundred personnel were involved.

*   *   *   *

A possum grumbled in his sleep and edged deeper into the cleft of the tall gum tree's branches; a lyre bird streaked into the clump of ferns as the convoy rumbled up the narrow track and into the clearing. Men clambered out of buses and milled around in a mixture of shouted orders and aimless activity. More vehicles nosed in among the confusion. Someone got a fire going and men huddled around its blaze, which began to dissipate the morning mist.

The clearing, some hundred metres across, was at the end of the slippery track up from the highway and it had hiking trails, neatly signposted by the Forestry Commission, radiating out into the thick bush. It was the obvious spot for the command post.

The crew of the mobile communication centre van imperiously occupied the centre of the clearing and began unpacking and bolting together huge aluminium aerial towers. Two buses, four police cars and three trucks were bullied into some semblance of neat lines around the edge and the canteen caravan was manhandled in beside the Command Caravan.

The possum grunted in sleepy disgust and moved further up the tree.

By ten a.m. the clearing was a bustling complex of activity. Various sections, each consisting of a student designated as 'sergeant' with five 'constables' and a portable radio, had been briefed and despatched into the dripping bush. A nervous student, designated as 'inspector in charge', was seated in the Command Caravan surrounded by wall-sized maps and chattering radios. Other students acted as runners, relaying messages from the field commanders. Vehicles roared in and out of the clearing as radio messages came back from field units reporting sightings of the fugitive offenders. The communications caravan nestled under a swaying arabesque of forty-foot aerial towers which gave them instant contact with all major police units in Australia. In the canteen caravan a bored junior constable dispensed plastic mugs of soup to damp police members reappearing from the mountain fog.

*   *   *   *

'Charles, it's a glorious day.'

Rodney swept back the gauze kitchen curtains of their tiny Carlton flat. Morning sunshine dappled the red brick terrace opposite.

Charles nodded and reflectively sipped his breakfast coffee.

'It's a day for *doing* things! Do you know,' Rodney paused for effect, 'I believe it might be the day for sending our little darlings out into the big, wide world!' He waved his hand over the dozen marijuana seedlings nestled in plastic pots on the kitchen window sill.

'You think they're big enough to plant out in the bush?'

'Yes, I do. And why not today? It's a Wednesday morning and there will be no tourists or horrid boy scouts tramping through that lovely little Forestry Reserve near Wallen. We could even pack a picnic lunch and wander through the trees until we find a secluded, leafy spot for our little babies to grow!'

Charles grunted and went to change into hiking boots.

*   *   *   *

Tiger Brennan won the guernsey of 'senior constable responsible for perimeter security'. It meant commanding a section of six 'constables' with the task of ensuring that the 'fugitives' did not desperately break into the Command Complex. They had instructions to patrol the perimeter and stop and search any person or vehicle approaching the clearing.

Fortuitously, Jerry Burke was appointed as his second-in-charge. They had been through rookie training together years ago and had since run small stations in adjoining towns in the back blocks of the Wimmera. Tiger took over Jerry's station during his annual leave and vice versa – each camping in the other's house and enjoying the generous living-away-from-home allowance provided by the Department.

In real life they were both sergeants but for the purposes of the exercise they wore no insignia. Jerry glanced meaningfully at Tiger's bush jacket which lacked the familiar three stripes. 'Senior Constable,' he said, 'how did we win this bloody job anyway? We're supposed to tramp round and round this damned clearing when it is obvious that the training staff are not going to tell their offenders to blunder in here. Can't we go and sit by the fire?'

Tiger returned the glance to Jerry's equally bare jacket shoulder. 'You baggy-arsed constables are paid to do what you're told, not to think about the god-like plans of the training staff. Now get your arse into gear and we'll do another circuit.'

They trudged off through the light scrub whose spiky leaves still dripped dew.

Despite the good-natured banter, Tiger was, in fact, uneasy. He was a good country cop who had no desire to rise to the rank of sub-officer and for years he had resisted the pressure to accept promotion to sergeant. Now he found himself the oldest member of the forty-man squad undergoing training. The younger students called him 'Dad' and he suspected that the sleek young senior sergeants of the training staff had little time for him. With some bitterness he pondered why they had allocated the field unit jobs to younger blokes and relegated him to the meaningless task of senior constable in charge of the perimeter guard.

He pressed forward through the light mist with his ragged line of men behind him. He paused at the sound of a vehicle. A battered Land Rover was labouring up the track to the clearing. He strode to the centre of the track and raised his hand in the traditional traffic policeman's command to halt.

'Jesus,' he muttered to Jerry beside him, 'they really do make these exercises realistic. The bloke behind the wheel has actually got a beard!' Turning to the driver, he said: 'I'm sorry, Sir, but I will have to ask you to produce your driver's licence and allow us to search the vehicle.'

He directed the driver to a gap between the Vehicle Recovery truck and the Dog Squad panel van whose occupant growled with interest. With shouted instructions from other constables the driver manoeuvred the vehicle into place and switched off the engine. Tiger looked into the driver's side window and said: 'Sir, are you all right?'

Rodney was surveying the bustling clearing with glazed eyes. His head swivelled and his mouth opened and shut silently. The perimeter security squad dutifully surrounded the vehicle. Another squad emerged from the trees. The huge Alsatian from the Dog Squad began eagerly sniffing the newly arrived vehicle. A cameraman from Public Relations Section took shots of the 'arrest', flash-bulb momentarily blinding. A reserve section jog-trotted past and into the scrub. The junior constable continued to dispense soup. The possum moved higher up the tree.

*   *   *   *

'Sarge, we've got a problem! There's a truck here with a load of pot plants.'

The training staff senior sergeant responsible for the smooth running of the exercise emerged from the Command Caravan impatiently.

'So what?' he snapped.

'No, Sarge, I mean *pot* plants. A couple of young blokes have arrived with seedlings for planting in the Reserve.'

The senior sergeant swore softly. To date the exercise had run well: Section #6 had bottled up the offenders in a gully and Section #4 were moving up to cut off the only escape route. Section #3 had discovered the nose-chipped body in a shallow grave and had secured the crime scene. Another half-an-hour and the troops could be recalled for debriefing . . . and now some idiots blunder in on it all.

He glanced uneasily at a number of senior officers dawdling around the soup caravan. In other circumstance he might have explained to the harmless owners of the cannabis that he was conducting an exercise and would appreciate it if they would quietly piss off and leave him alone. But a superintendent and even a deputy assistant commissioner appeared to be watching. He hesitated.

His hesitation was rendered redundant by a shriek of tyres as Rodney frantically reversed the Land Rover into the rear of the Dog Squad van, accelerated violently and hurtled down the muddy track, scattering the surrounding police aside.

Tiger shouted a message into his portable radio. At precisely the speed of light it transmitted across the two metres of air to the Communication Caravan. The eager radio crew swung into action, alerting all cars patrolling the suburbs of Alice Springs, then of West Perth, and eventually, after some confusion, the police station three kilometres down the track from the Forestry Reserve. There, a bored policeman took the message, ambled out of the station and, as instructed, parked his car across the only track which led to the highway and waited.

*   *   *   *

'Charles?'

The cells are made of cement brick and are bitterly cold on an Autumn night. Rodney perched on the bunk, knees under his chin and a smelly blanket clutched around his shoulders. They had not spoken for half-an-hour.

'Charles,' he repeated tentatively, 'who did you tell about our plans for the plants?'

'That's what I was going to ask *you*,' he snapped, '*I* told no-one.'

They sat in silence, eyes occasionally sliding suspiciously in each other's direction.

'Then *who* tipped them off?'

16

RIOT CONTROL

Colonialism is intrinsically evil: the imposition of the values and needs of the ruling classes of one nation upon the peoples of another. But being grubbily involved in it does not preclude you from watching, listening and musing on its various manifestations. My own experience is limited to the South Pacific. I am too racially prejudiced to make any dispassionate comment on the North Americans, who are beyond the pale, but it always seemed to me that the British colonial administrators were paternalistically condescending, the French insufferably detached and arrogant, the Spanish vicious and the Dutch despicable in their mean-minded shopkeeper's greed. (I speak of the personnel of colonial administrations, not of the citizens of the nations which they represented. In the South Pacific I developed a healthy distaste for the Dutch for example, and when, later in life, I eventually travelled to Europe, I was taken aback by the gentleness and civility of the citizens of Amsterdam.) The British administrators managed to maintain their control over vast areas by ineffable faith in their own superiority, a condescending but often shrewd insight into the internal power structures of the societies which they ruled, plus what can only be described as outrageous bluff.

Australia's one and only foray into colonialism was its mandated rule of Papua New Guinea – the southern half from the turn of the century and the northern half from 1914 – until Papua New Guinea became an independent nation in 1975. The style of administration broadly followed the British pattern with slight changes in the admixture of components: the sense of superiority was similar but without the pomposity, the shrewd insight into what was going on at the grassroots level was sharper and there was much, much more use of cheerful, larrikin bluff.

The country was divided into Districts (now the Provinces of independent Papua New Guinea) each administered by a District Commissioner – the 'DC' or, in the creole language of Papua New Guinea, the *Nambawan Kiap* (literally, the 'number-one patrol officer'). Personnel of the administrative structure that he controlled were all members of the central public service: his police force consisted of 'field detachments' of the Royal Papua New Guinea Constabulary, his medical personnel were technically responsible to Health Department headquarters, his teachers and clerks belonged to the Education Department, the Tax Department and the like, and he himself was a representative of the Department of District Administration. However, the brutal topography of Papua New Guinea – which precludes any real road system and certainly no railway system – meant that many of the Districts were isolated and administered with a degree of autonomy which would terrify an Australian bureaucrat fixated on uniformity and centralised control.

The national capital was Port Moresby but in the outlying Districts – especially in the rugged Highlands where contact with the capital was cumbersome and limited – the DC's role was sometimes akin to that of a feudal lord. The tone of colonial control in a particular District was often shaped by the personality of its *Nambawan Kiap*. For example, one such DC in the Western Highlands was something of a legend in the 1960s for his firmness, fairness and flamboyance. I have heard the story told many times, and with many embellishments, of an incident in which he left an official reception with a large number of whiskies under his belt and dismissed his police chauffeur and insisted on driving the official car home on his own. A young, indigenous constable, on mobile patrol in the District capital, noted a vehicle being driven erratically and pulled it over. As the constable approached, the window on the driver's side wound down slowly to reveal the face of the *Nambawan Kiap*. 'Oh, my god!' the constable gasped. 'Yes,' growled the DC, 'I *am*. And don't you ever forget it, son!' The window wound up and the car drove on.

Outside the District capitals, each District comprised a number of Sub-Districts, each managed by an Assistant District Commissioner (ADC) – the *Nambatu Kiap*. While the DCs had a high degree of autonomy, this was *a fortiori* so for the ADCs administering Sub-Districts in the roadless Highlands. Some were areas where patrol posts had been established only in the 1950s among people many of whom had never experienced any significant interaction with white-skins. ('Areas recently under Administration influence' was the classification in the official records.)

One such Sub-District embraced a string of high-altitude valleys inhabited by people whose collective number would be roughly equivalent to that of a major provincial city in Australia. Apart from twice-daily radio contact with District Headquarters, its only link with the outside world was the frighteningly tiny airstrip frowned upon by encircling mountains whose peaks were often swathed in cloud. The ADC had a staff of two or three white-skinned teachers, a couple of white nursing sisters, a few black paramedics and a detachment of black police.

I first visited Sub-District Headquarters in April 1972 when the Supreme Court had to hold a sitting there to deal with a couple of murder charges and a few lesser matters. On 25 April the judge was obliged to adjourn the court for one day as written directives from the Port Moresby headquarters of Department of District Administration, delivered by the twice-weekly mail plane, required the ADC to declare a public holiday for Anzac Day. To me, that day is the sadly glorious celebration of Australia's military tradition which, paradoxically, commemorates the slaughter of thousands of Australian soldiers as a result of the incompetence of the generals of Australia's colonial master, Britain. In the remote Sub-District the Anzac Day ceremony commenced at ten a.m. as the last of the mists moved up the valleys. The parade ground outside the administration building had been freshly mown, making stark and pointed the white-washed flagpole. The children from the primary school, shepherded by their teachers, marched in to form a series of lines behind the flagpole. There was something insanely incongruous about these giggling, bare-footed kids, dressed in khaki shorts or light cotton frocks, pacing in military quick-march time. The ADC made a brief speech and the six members of his police detachment, standing at attention before the flagpole in their crisp blue uniforms and glistening army gaiters, did a formal 'present arms' with their rifles as the Australian flag was lowered to half-mast. The police bugler played the 'Last Post' and the school kids shrieked with glee, knowing that this meant the end of the ceremony and the beginning of a half-day off from school. Later that day I yarned with local people, learning that the only people present who had experienced anything of Australia's military tradition was the judge (who, I knew, had served as a sergeant in the Artillery during World War II, never leaving Australia) and the older sergeant of the police detachment, who, in 1942, had been co-opted at pistol point as a carrier for the Australian troops. The older people of this valley remembered only sporadic contact with the two opposing armies in World War II. They found the Japanese soldiers rather congenial because of their formal politeness, which contrasted with the uncouthness of the members of the few Australian patrols which penetrated the valley.

The judge and I were billeted in the ADC's house. He was a short, chunky Australian who, like most *kiaps*, had done his training at the Australian School of Pacific Administration in Sydney and enlisted as an enthusiastic officer with the lowly rank of assistant patrol officer. He had done his apprenticeship in a number of Districts of Papua New Guinea and now, in his mid to late twenties, found himself with personal responsibility for the administration of a massive and isolated area of the Highlands. He had moved gently and learnt fluency in the local language. With his detachment of six police, he hardly represented the military might of colonial power but the elders of the valleys respected him and accepted him as a symbol of authority. The provision of a medical clinic and a school were welcomed but more important, in the eyes of the elders, was his role as a figurehead of stable government. He rarely interfered in their lives other than to act as an independent arbiter in disputes between the clans and to proclaim the sanctity of the Government Law. It did lessen the incessant inter-clan warfare, which was the plague of life in the valleys.

When on duty his six constables always wore the smart blue-black uniform of the Royal Papua New Guinea Constabulary and carried their aging .303 Lee-Enfield rifles. The burnished brass of the buckles of their black gaiters and belts would have warmed the heart of any army sar-major and the wooden sheathing of the Lee-Enfields glowed from repeated polishing with linseed oil. In fact the rifles were usually unloaded. After a few unfortunate incidents of constables shooting themselves in the foot during training exercises with live ammunition, the ADC now rarely unlocked the magazine and issued cartridges. That was of no consequence. The rifles were carried ceremoniously, like the *fasci* of imperial Rome, as the symbol of Law and Order.

I learnt from the local staff the story of the last outbreak of tribal warfare which had occurred some months previously. It had been a minor matter with little blood shed. Apparently tensions between two clans had bubbled to the point where some thirty young warriors from each clan had ignored the directives of the elders and had assembled in full battle formation. They were armed with machetes and the huge and deadly longbows of the Highlands with their four-foot-long unfletched arrows. As usual, they had spent several days before the appointed time of battle preparing themselves and they were truly formidable: eyes circled in white ochre which contrasted with the glistening black face paint of pig fat and ground charcoal, and the massive headdresses of Bird of Paradise plumes making them look seven feet tall.

The two lines of warriors assembled, facing each other across a clearing a few kilometres from the Sub-District headquarters. As usual, the 'fight leader' of one line stepped forward and, in the yodelling chant of the local language used on solemn occasions, proclaimed the justice of the cause of his clan, its superior fighting prowess and the inevitable death of its enemies. A swell of grumbled approval rose from the ranks of his men as they thumped the base of arrows against the ground and a swell of taunts and jeers rose from the other line. Its fight leader stepped forward and proclaimed the justice of his cause at length. A few arrows were fired from both sides, inflicting flesh wounds, and the two leaders resumed their operatic dialogue at greater volume.

A runner from one of the villages reached Sub-District headquarters to tell the ADC that negotiations appeared to be breaking down and it could erupt into a full-blown massacre. The ADC and his police detachment climbed aboard the four-wheel-drive vehicle.

They drove slowly and deliberately between the lines, stopping at the rear end of the clearing. The six constables alighted and formed a line, checking their spacing and responding to the command 'Dress by the right!' until it was an immaculate parade-ground line. Some of the younger warriors gazed with admiration at their precision and fearlessness. On the clipped commands of the ADC they came to the 'At ease' position, then to a sharp 'Atten-shun!' and 'Order arms!', rifle butts thumping the ground simultaneously. Finally the ADC shouted the command 'Port arms!' and they stood as an implacable line, with feet apart, burnished rifles clutched firmly against their chests at a forty-five degree angle. A few warriors fidgeted with envy.

Slowly the ADC paced to the centre of the clearing precisely mid-way between the two fight leaders. In the operatic chant of the local language he summarised the bases of the dispute between the clans, ponderously specifying the pros and cons of each clan's contentions. It took some ten minutes. Then, with rhetorical flourish, he eulogised the fighting prowess of both clans and the wisdom of their elders. Finally he expounded the sanctity of the Government Law and gravely announced his disappointment that two such dignified clans would ignore the advice of their elders and lower themselves to the bloodshed which would solve nothing and only exacerbate the tensions with the inevitable payback killings. That, he added, was more characteristic of the 'rubbish' clans of other valleys.

He lowered his voice and addressed both fight leaders. Muttered negotiations went on for some twenty minutes. Eventually one of the fight leaders pondered in silence for some time and then made the classically symbolic action of taking an arrow and breaking it over his knee. The other watched, took a deep breath and, matching his dignity, did the same. Some warriors laid down their bows. The six constables stood firmly and impassively, their rifles still in the 'port arms' position.

Reverting to the creole language normally used by *kiaps*, the ADC addressed all sixty warriors and the throngs of women, children and elderly people watching anxiously from the protection of the jungle which surrounded the clearing. Resolution of important disputes by uncivilised warfare, he thundered, would not be tolerated in *this* Sub-District – the most dignified Sub-District in the Western Highlands.

In his ex officio capacity as Field Commander of the Royal Papua New Guinea Constabulary detachment, he announced that all sixty warriors were under arrest, charged with 'Riotous affray' under the *Summary Offences Act*.

Then, in his ex officio capacity as Local Magistrate, he declared the bush clearing to be a sitting of the Local Court. He observed that there was convincing evidence of riotous affray, pronounced all defendants guilty, and sentenced them to one month's imprisonment with hard labour. The fight leaders nodded with approval.

In his ex officio capacity as Field Commander of the Royal Papua New Guinea Prisons Service he paused in brief silence to conceal a minor embarrassment. The Sub-District prison was a rough dormitory shed enclosed by a few symbolic strands of barbed wire. At the most, it could accommodate thirty sleeping mats.

Reverting to his capacity as ADC, he ordered one line of thirty warriors to do a left-turn and march to the prison compound, leaving their weapons at the entrance. With an eye to the impassive six constables, they did a passable attempt at a parade-ground left-turn and marched out of the clearing.

Turning to the other line, he told them that he did not have the facilities to deal with them at the moment. They would, he directed, present themselves at the prison compound in four week's time to serve their sentence. He barked the command 'Dismiss!' at the six constables who did a smart right-turn and climbed into the vehicle.

At daybreak precisely one month later the prisoners assembled inside the gate. They talked excitedly with much banter about getting home to their wives and children. They were lithe and fit after four weeks on the government rations of tinned fish and rice supplemented by fresh vegetables grown in the prison compound. The lawns of the administration building were immaculate and the partly constructed road over the mountain, which would eventually connect with the next valley, had progressed several kilometres. Ceremonially the ADC opened the unlocked gate of the prison compound and they filed out. Members of the other clan, standing in a huddle a few hundred metres away, waited until all the prisoners had departed and then filed into the compound. They set to work laying out their sleeping mats and checking out the healthy vegetable garden which the previous batch of prisoners had planted within the enclosure delineated by three strands of barbed wire.

The ADC silently counted the newcomers. Precisely thirty. Not necessarily the same thirty individuals whom he had sentenced but that was of no consequence: the clan would never consider losing face by failing to match the other clan in providing thirty warriors to serve their sentence with dignity.

The ADC closed the prison gate. Honour had been satisfied on all sides and, at least for a while, peace reigned in the valleys.

17

GUBBA

The tyres hummed rhythmically on the bitumen. The last of Darwin's straggling suburbs fell behind and the endless undulation of scrubby plain unfolded.

He relaxed into the seat, right foot sprawled immobile on the accelerator. Two hundred and thirty miles. The Darwin to Katherine run was a long drive to do alone but not a demanding one: the sealed highway occasionally curved lazily, one saw another vehicle every half-hour or so, and there was little to do but sit, like the driver of an interstate locomotive, and gaze at the anonymous scrub slipping past.

He should, he thought, be more uneasy about this trip. The instructions from head office were damned silly: look after the Katherine office for a week or more until the district welfare officer is discharged from hospital. Head office should know that he was a city-trained social worker who could, more or less, handle his work with the urbanised part-Aboriginals of Darwin, but Katherine was deep in cattle country. Most of the people there, for whom the Department had a responsibility, were full-bloods with deep tribal ties. He knew nothing of their world and was an absurd choice as a fill-in for the local officer in charge.

He had no skills to handle the job and would, he thought to himself, probably bungle it. But, just now, he found it hard to knot his mind into anxious anticipation. Perhaps it was the solemn purr of the vehicle's motor. Perhaps it was the glow of orange on the passing, mine-scarred hillocks as afternoon eased into evening.

A kangaroo bounded across the road. He squeezed the brake pedal gently – the road was a symmetrical strip flanked by a carpet of scrub and he was able to see the roo several hundred metres ahead. But he held the vehicle at lowered speed remembering that it was sunset and other roos, and probably cattle, would be likely to blunder over the highway at this time of day.

In fact an old brumby stumbled out of the scrub and into his path a few miles south of Pine Creek. He slowed, honked the horn, and the horse flinched and disappeared into the darkening bush. Having slowed the vehicle to walking pace he impulsively braked to a complete halt. He studied the diagram on the gear shift knob and the little yellow button on the gear box casing. In his normal job in Darwin he drove a frumpy Ford sedan and had never had control of one of these tank-like things used by the patrol officers on bush work. With adolescent curiosity he fumbled the gear stick into the low ratio/four wheel drive mode. The gear box whined and the vehicle moved ahead with the inexorable steadiness of a battleship. Satisfied, he returned to two-wheel drive and settled back into a smooth, humming run down the deserted highway.

Occasionally the headlights picked out the mirrored pin-points of the eyes of a wandering brumby or kangaroo but, for the most part, only a flickering stream of the tips of stunted bushes unreeled. He lit a cigarette, settled deeper into the seat and tried to concentrate his mind. At one level, he pondered, this week has all the makings of an embarrassing fiasco; yet, on another level, it was a break from the sordid stupidity of the Darwin office and couldn't be all that bad.

Eventually the tyres thumped on the cement of the bridge over the Katherine River and the lights of the township emerged. Kirby's pub was officially closed but there were lights on and he booked into a room and slept.

In the morning he found the Katherine office virtually deserted, apart from the typist and some fleeting persons. The child care officer – a middle-aged lady who would have looked less incongruous in a Wagnerian opera – introduced herself brusquely and informed him that she was required to spend a few days at Adelaide River checking on some multi-problem families; to his relief, she left. The typist explained that all three patrol officers were out bush, doing the routine inspection of the housing provided for Aboriginal stockmen on the cattle stations. Each of them, she said, had taken a swag and field rations in a quantity which would suggest that they would be unlikely to return within the week. That left only the Black Tracker. The Department, in its benevolence, had redesignated the position as: 'Patrol Assistant, Class II', and Daniel sat immobile, in neatly ironed khakis, at a desk by the window.

Daniel eyed the temporary boss impassively.

He, in turn, introduced himself, sat opposite Daniel and inquired about the current situation in the sub-district. He was surprised by Daniel's helpfulness. In an accent which oscillated between the gentle lilt of the Wailbri language and pedantic school-taught English, Daniel briefed him on what was likely to be required over the next couple of days. Wednesday would be quiet: it was still another couple of weeks before cattle mustering on the stations would be completed and few ringers would be in town. Thursday was pension day and there would be the usual influx of tribal relatives, the inevitable brawls and 'Drunk and Disorderly' charges and the predictable requests for the district welfare officer to attend the local police station.

He listened to Daniel carefully, trying to conceal his awkwardness. He had grown up within a narrow, Anglo-Saxon culture and, confronted by the gentle firmness of someone whose cheeks glistened black, had no rubrics for easy dialogue. He wavered between the condescension of a senior officer struggling to maintain control of an unfamiliar situation and the mindless romanticism of a middle-class white responding to the inscrutability of an older black. Daniel addressed him by his first name – rather than the familiar term 'Boss' – but did so without the obsequiousness of someone coyly establishing familiarity. Nor was it the manipulativeness of someone who needs to covertly despise. They talked at length.

At the end of the day he returned to Kirby's pub, softly elated. In the evenings the bar of Batt Kirby's pub would be the noisiest, clattering concatenation of drinkers in any hotel in Australia. Half-blood ringers arguing raucously with stolid Irish/Australian road-train drivers, wispy white clerks from the public service giggling with hairy buffalo shooters and the jumbled noise bouncing off the glistening walls coated in lettuce-green enamel. He sank a final rum, extricated himself from a convoluted political discussion with a couple of Swedish drillers from one of the mining exploration companies and, again, slept deeply.

In the morning the office was occupied by only Daniel and the typist. He nodded to them, settled himself at the desk and began working through the 'IN' basket.

Two inches down through the pile he came across a memo from the local police, dated some ten days before, routinely reporting an alleged murder. Legislation required that the Welfare Department conduct a supplementary investigation into the circumstances of any serious offence involving full-blood Aborigines. He riffled through the papers. It was the usual stuff: some fool had got himself drunk out of his mind, had taunted another equally drunk bloke around the campfire and had ended up with his skull caved in.

He glanced over to Daniel at the opposite desk. 'We've got to do a report for the court.'

'What name?'

He read out the name of the deceased in clumsy phonetic pronunciation.

Daniel frowned. 'Yeah, I know that one.'

'Well we've got to check out the circumstances before it goes to court. The bloke is being held on remand in Fanny Bay Gaol, Darwin; he is scheduled to front the Magistrates Court on . . .' he checked the file, 'Er . . . two days ago. But when he gets to the Supreme Court they will want a report on the social background. Do you know where the "high level camp" is?'

Daniel nodded without condescension. Entry to the township of Katherine during the dry season is via the concrete road bridge across the river and, during the wet season floods, via the spindly wooden railway bridge which towers between the two banks. The main camping ground of the fringe-dwelling Aboriginal people, he explained, moves with the seasons – the high level camp or the low level camp, according to whether the road bridge is open.

'We'd better have a look at it,' he said, 'it's an ordinary one but I'd better get some details on family background, tribal affiliations and all that, for the sake of the file.'

Daniel rose and got the ignition keys to the patrol vehicle.

The high level camp was a dusty clearing whose indeterminate boundaries merged with the ragged eucalypts. Smoke drifted lethargically from two campfires. Dogs barked and scampered at the intrusion. An old lady squatted immobile, sucking on a pipe without discernible movement of her lips. Children gathered around them.

He watched Daniel moving among the corrugated-iron humpies talking softly in a language which he did not understand. Feeling a little irrelevant, he sat on the running-board of the vehicle and lit a cigarette. He gazed at the circle of jostling, curious children. The twin candles of snot from each set of flared nostrils were unpleasant: the long, curving eyelashes around each set of wide, curious eyes were enchanting.

Daniel heaved himself back into the vehicle with a terse: 'OK, we can go now'.

He started the engine and said: 'Got enough detail for a report? We don't need much. No complicated stuff, eh?'

Daniel stared ahead. 'No, Boss, this is blackfeller business. He was sung.'

They drove in silence for a few minutes and then he pulled the vehicle over to the side of the road, switched off the engine and tacitly, with his eyes, requested more information. He had a vague knowledge from the anthropological journals of the practice of the elders of a tribe 'singing' a person to death: ritually demanding the death of an offender who, with no alternative, accepted that decree and obediently died.

Daniel outlined the local situation patiently and lucidly. In the Katherine area serious breaches of ancient tribal law were not handled by the superficial stuff portrayed in television documentaries: it was rather more complex. The person who had been 'sung' accepted the sentence of death and, sometimes, simply wasted away, eating and drinking nothing. More often, he unconsciously arranged his death by getting drunk and going to sleep in the centre of the highway or with his head on the railway line, or even by taunting the local 'heavy' during one of the drunken parties around the campfire. For someone not fully accepting of tribal authority there were more complex methods: a blow to the back of the head and an elaborate ritual which left a small incision on the lower-left abdomen of the condemned man – physically harmless but spiritually an inexorable demand for a quick death.

'So how do we know whether this was just another drunken brawl or a tribal execution?'

Daniel displayed no impatience. 'We check on whether he has any small cuts on him, of course.'

They drove to the hospital.

Their request was routine and the doctor ushered them into the tiny morgue, indicated the appropriate drawer of the deep freeze and left them alone.

The drawers were similar to the filing cabinets in head office except that this one unrolled and unrolled to reveal the full repose of a naked, tall man who stared upwards with clouded eyeballs. The splintered concavity in the forehead was packed with cotton wool; other wads of cotton wool were stuffed into the nostrils to prevent the seepage of body fluids.

The surgical cut from throat to genitals, for the post-mortem check on internal organs, had been roughly stitched back together again. The blue/black penis was puckered and curled in a nest of pubic hair. He had never been in the situation of studying another man's genitals close up and he was uneasy, hoping that Daniel had not noted his gazing.

They checked the body inch by inch. Clumsily they manhandled it over on to its face in the narrow filing cabinet and checked the back and buttocks.

Finally they pushed the drawer backwards: it trundled smoothly on oiled rollers until the cover clicked into place as one of four anonymous rectangles in the wall of the freezer room. They found the doctor in his office, thanked him and stepped out into the sunshine.

They were momentarily aware of the harshness of the sun on their cheeks, abrasive but clear. Their boots scuffed up powdery dust as they walked across the car park.

'So, there were no unusual incisions: so it was an ordinary brawl?'

Daniel shrugged. 'So they didn't need to do the full ritual.'

*   *   *   *

After the evening meal he had the mandatory couple of beers with the blokes in the public bar and withdrew to his room and slept.

Twice he woke, lips quivering and straining to scream but clogged in the treacle of movement in a dream. A tall, silent figure, blurred into the surrounding darkness but focussed by the stark white cotton wool plugged into each nostril, shuffled implacably towards him.

On the third approach he shook himself awake and stumbled out of bed. He rummaged through his pack and found the flask of rum always kept there – affectionately known as 'the survival kit' – and searched for a glass. The tiny room contained no such luxuries but did have a desk by the window. He pulled the curtains back, settled at the desk, lit a cigarette and watched the beginnings of piccaninny dawn glow through the trees on the other side of the railway track. He sipped at the flask of rum. The nightmare was, he assured himself, nothing to be ashamed of: he had never had much occasion to handle dead human beings. Grandad had been discreetly removed from the farm house by a blank-faced undertaker and his eight-year-old mind had recorded only the smell of fresh varnish. That road accident victim, a couple of years ago, had been swept under hygienic sheets by the ambulance officers before he could offer help. He had, after all, conducted himself with dignity in front of Daniel; he was, he insisted, handling an unfamiliar situation with rational competence.

Full dawn illuminated the deep reds and olives of the angular trees. He dressed and went looking for breakfast.

He spent the morning working through the pile of files, sometimes irritated by the clack, clack, clack of the typist at the front desk and all of the time aware of Daniel's static presence at the desk by the window. The typist was able to take shorthand dictation but he wrote the report for the court in long hand, uneasy about dictating phrases like: 'Routine homicide: no specific anthropological implications', in Daniel's hearing.

The next file concerned pension cheques not reaching some old people who were camped on the fringe of a cattle station further south of Katherine. He asked Daniel if he knew the area.

Daniel's eyes brightened. 'Yeah, I know that place. Good country. That's *my* country.'

They calculated that it would be a full day trip there and back and agreed to leave at first light the next day.

He returned to the pub in the evening and shared a noisy meal with a couple of stock and station agents. Foolishly he let slip which department he worked for and found himself being regaled by vehement, and sometimes incoherent, sermons about the dangers of the Aboriginal land rights movement. He used the excuse of an early start next day to withdraw from the dining room and have a solitary nightcap in the bar. Prudently, he sank three rums before retiring and woke only once at the approach of the figure with the clouded eye balls and cotton wool. The rest of the night was just sluggish restlessness.

Daniel picked him up at the pub shortly after dawn. He had planned to meet Daniel at the office but the patrol vehicle was washed, filled with petrol and Daniel seemed eager to move.

Again, the tyres hummed rhythmically on the bitumen; again, the township slipped away and was replaced by flickering scrub.

South of Katherine, the plains were even flatter, the scrub more sparse. Empty beer cans littered the edge of the slide-rule-straight highway. The crest of each slight rise revealed the same panorama as the previous one: sprawling plain and spindly bush.

Routinely they changed seats at the end of the first hour and he slumped in the passenger seat while Daniel drove. The unreeling but unchanging backdrop of stunted bush, rock and sand was hypnotic and he began to doze. Then he became aware that Daniel was talking to him quietly.

'That place,' said Daniel, stabbing an index finger against the windscreen and indicating an area of the blurred horizon, 'is where the Two Sisters camped during the Dreamtime.'

He nodded appreciatively and squinted into the mid-morning glare. The limitless plain lazed in the sunshine, too big and too still to be organised into the quadrants of a surveyor's map. It sprawled timelessly. And, to him, blankly.

'And you see, Boss, now we're moving into Wailbri country: see how different it is from the Katherine bush?'

He listened to Daniel's voice. He noted the way Daniel unconsciously slipped into using the term 'boss', rather than addressing him by his first name, when talking of things privy to his people. He noted Daniel's trust and desire to share important things with a temporary travelling companion. He was honoured and struggled to respond but had no words. He grunted his interest.

The vehicle swerved to the edge of the highway and braked to a halt. 'I want to show you something', Daniel beamed.

He uncoiled stiff limbs and clambered out, wincing at the harshness of the sun which had been masked by air whistling through the moving vehicle. In the absence of the steady hum of the motor the silence hovered tangibly. They were the centre of a circle of flat bushland which stretched infinitely outwards.

Daniel beckoned. 'This is the spring where the Great Snake came up to the surface during the Dreamtime.'

He followed. Ten or fifteen metres from the edge of the road there was a clump of rocks surrounded by scrawny trees. The sand was powdery and red. A lizard darted across a tattered, flattened box of Kleenex tissues. A few rusting beer cans glinted in response to the blazing sun. The silence was implacable.

'See, Boss?'

'Well, yes, mate. Thanks.'

Near-noon sun burnt into their unprotected cheeks. He shuffled and swatted at a fly nuzzling around his eye-lid. 'It's good, Daniel . . . but, well, I don't really understand it all . . .' His voice dissipated in the blinding sunshine.

Daniel stood in thought. 'Yes, I know', he said softly.

18

JUDICIAL DISCREETNESS

I suppose you could say that he loved her. At the time, he probably would not have described it that way. He was a morose bachelor, painfully awkward in relationships with women. He had been through training in a theological seminary and then through a marriage which had crumbled into divorce. His tattered soul was cluttered with the emotional baggage of guilt, striving and restless yearning. Sharon never asked about his background. Sometimes, when a puffing orgasm has subsided, she would touch his cheek and say: 'Hey, that was nice', with a simplicity which made all his strivings rather silly.

In strictly objective terms, I suppose you could say that they had little in common apart from complementary genitalia, a mute trust in each other's reality and the shared situation of being white-skinned isolates wandering irrelevantly around Papua New Guinea in the year before it became an independent nation. She was working as a barmaid in the 'Bird of Paradise Hotel' in Goroka.

'Sharon, I've been assigned to the Eastern Highlands circuit this month. Will you still be in Goroka?'

'You've been what? Bloody hell, speak louder! I suppose you're phoning from Port Moresby. The coons are running the radio-telephone set-up these days. I can't hear anything but static!'

He winced, conscious of the fact that the locally born radio operator would probably be listening in.

'The Supreme Court ... circuit in the Eastern Highlands Province ... a couple of murder trials in Goroka which could drag on for three weeks ... I'll be there by the end of the week.'

'Beaut!' she said. Or something like that: the radio-telephone transmission was indeed bad.

He made the travel arrangements for the Supreme Court party. The judge was a locum tenens from the Australian courts, filling in while the judge from the Papua New Guinea Supreme Court took two months' leave. The new judge's first month of circuit work had involved constant travelling on the outstations but, with the second month scheduled for the comparative luxury of living in a hotel in Goroka, he had invited his wife to join him. They met her off the plane from Australia. She was a beautiful woman. They must have been in their late forties but were like a pair of adolescents in their patent joy at being reunited. As the austere 'minder' to the judge, he winced as they openly held hands in the airport lobby and talked excitedly about the prospect of being together for a month in the exotic Highlands. They all shared drinks in the airport lounge. A wife of a Supreme Court judge is typically rather supercilious towards her husband's Associate but she was charming: she plied him with questions about life in Papua New Guinea, about his own role in the administration of the Supreme Court, and what they might expect to see in the course of the circuit.

On arrival in the Highlands the next day he ushered the judge and his wife from the air strip and into a police car and then carried their luggage into the suite at the 'Royal' – the only other hotel in Goroka. Once they were settled he pointed out that the court would not be convened until the next morning and asked to be excused for the evening.

The lounge bar at the 'Bird of Paradise' is a dimly lit cavern of tatty ornateness. Sharon presided: refusing to serve the more obviously drunken clients, cheerfully ignoring the comments from the others about the magnificent pair of breasts which strained against her low-cut dress, and bullying the bar-boys into emptying ashtrays and collecting empty glasses.

He entered, she nodded, poured him a beer in silence and returned to her customers. At closing time she locked the doors, opened a bottle of Bacardi and they sat, swapping gossip about mutual friends among the shifting, restless tribe of white-skins who formed the infrastructure of a fading colonial service. Brenda had gone south and was working in Canberra; Charles had gone

112

troppo and was living in a religious community in India; Gavin had gone gay and was having an affair with an assistant Crown prosecutor in Port Moresby. They gossiped for hours.

Rain padded on the roof. She explained that the hotel management provided her with only a dingy room shared with another barmaid. They walked through the rain back to his bungalow at the 'Royal'.

Like so many ex-Christians, especially ex-seminarians, his soul was a taut tangle when it came to happy, uncommitted sex. Sharon simply loved and never understood his scruples. And his awkwardness always evaporated at her warmth. They shared gleeful communion.

Dining arrangements for the two- or three-week stay posed problems. The aide-de-camp to a Supreme Court judge is expected to dine with His Honour and His Wife when they are living in hotels on circuit. The next day he mentioned to them that he had discovered an old friend living in Goroka and asked to be excused from the evening meal. The judge countered by suggesting that he invite the friend to join them all. Reluctantly he agreed, silently wondering how Sharon would fit in with the chit chat of a formal dinner with a Supreme Court judge. His worries turned out to be groundless. The judge and his wife responded warmly to Sharon's directness and cheerful frankness, sensing a familiar reality in a strange land. It was a happy evening of animated conversation. The judge's wife was delighted with Sharon's offer to show her around the local market in the morning. Within a few days they were good friends, sharing gossip and secrets like a pair of gleeful schoolgirls relishing a holiday in an anonymous resort. They settled into the ritual of all meeting for dinner each evening.

But sleeping arrangements posed a problem. Like many hotels in Papua New Guinea, the 'Royal' consisted of a central building containing the kitchen, bar and dining room, surrounded by a clutter of small bungalows in which the guests slept. At the end of each evening meal he would thank the judge and his wife for their company and ask to be excused while he escorted Sharon back to her hotel. For the sake of decorum, they would walk once around the garden and then slip surreptitiously back and into his bungalow. Sharon would disappear before breakfast. The judge was a gentleman: almost certainly aware of the reality but sufficiently discreet to conceal his awareness.

In the second week the hotel manager explained that a large party of Japanese tourists was arriving and it would be necessary to re-arrange the allocation of bungalows. That evening they dined on the verandah to avoid the shrill noise of the tourists. The food was excellent. The judge's wife gossiped happily with Sharon. The Associate discussed cases with His Honour. Monsoon rain dribbled languidly down the verandah posts. The manager appeared and gave them keys to the re-allocated bungalows, explaining that their luggage had been transferred accordingly. After the third glass of port Sharon and the Associate rose and excused themselves.

They did the ritual circumnavigation of the hotel and stopped in the darkness at the edge of the hotel compound and examined the number on the new key. 'Bloody hell!' murmured Sharon. The bungalow to which he had been allocated was all of six feet from the edge of the verandah where the judge and his wife were lingering over coffee. They got down on hands and knees and crawled cautiously, keeping within the shadow cast by the verandah whose floor stood several feet above the ground. The rear wall of the squat, square bungalow faced the verandah with its door on the opposite side, but there was still the problem of getting to the door. They could only crawl the length of the verandah and around the side wall of the bungalow. 'Bloody hell!' Sharon grated, grazing a knee on the roots of the Banyan tree which abutted the verandah rail. The side with the door on it was invisible to His Honour and his wife but still in clear view of the other bungalows which were spread around the compound. He raised himself on his knees, like a dog begging for a biscuit, and fumblingly got the key into the lock. They prised the door open and crawled inside, prudently leaving the light off.

Sharon does not lie on a bed: she sprawls. She was warm and enveloping. Some people are gentle and accepting in they way they speak and carry themselves but demanding and

114

domineering in their secret souls: Sharon is the other way around. They made love. She groaned, he panted.

The usual vacuum flask of iced water, supplied by the hotel management, stood upon the chest of drawers which was placed across the end of the bed. Instinctively he braced the souls of his feet against its wooden surface in the final thrust. Sharon moaned. He pushed.

The vacuum flask shattered onto the top of the rocking chest of drawers. Iced water and broken glass exploded across a tangle of legs and buttocks. With the shock, they climaxed simultaneously, howling in unison like a pair of demon-possessed dingoes.

Lights winked on in the surrounding bungalows. There were questioning shouts. Anxious people padded through the darkness outside. Sharon and he clung together wetly, silently refusing to acknowledge concerned tapping on the bungalow door.

At breakfast nothing was said. At some point the judge's wife murmured: 'Did you get Sharon back to her hotel safely?' He nodded mutely. He was sure he could detect a gentle inward smile on the face of the judge who wordlessly poured him black coffee.

He has long since lost contact with Sharon. But perhaps an important part of love is shared inconsequential memories.

19

AFTERNOON SHIFT

Some – though not many – members of the training staff of the Recruit Academy imagine that they train recruits for their future profession. In fact that period of several months at the Academy is a 'rite of passage' which ceremonially confirms the careful selection of applicants. It offers a new self-identity in the form of a blue uniform, a heightened level of physical fitness, a smattering of legal jargon and an ability to march in step with the rest of the squad. The real training takes place on the stations after graduation. The less fortunate junior constables flounder in the unpredictability of 'general duties' work on the streets; those stations designated as 'training stations' are almost always the busiest ones in tough areas. Some crack and drop out, some forge their own professional identity, others withdraw into a constricted role of cynical self-preservation, or else into that of the 'cowboy' crime fighter – a role delineated more by North American television than by the realities of police work in Australia. The luckier ones are taken under the wing of older members who provide tacit support and a rough but committed introduction to professionalism. Within the privacy of gossip-sharing between trainee constables over the mess room table, it is not unusual for the term 'my father' to be used quite unselfconsciously in talking about one's more-experienced partner. In observing this sort of interaction one is inclined to think of the analogy of the classic medieval conception of the master/apprentice relationship but it is a little more complex than that: in police work, such bonds, formed early in one's career, often grow into a nexus of reciprocal loyalty and support which endures until retirement.

*   *   *   *

Mechanically Ken went through the ritual of clocking on for the three-to-eleven shift on the section car: skim-read the telex messages, draw equipment and check the Occurrences Book from the day shift. He lumbered into the mess room like a mobile Christmas tree festooned with baton, handcuffs and holstered revolver in one hand, preliminary breath test kit and pen in the other, leather-sheathed portable radio dangling from its straps over one shoulder and clipboard tucked precariously under the other arm. He dumped it all with a clatter on the table of the empty mess room and made a cup of coffee.

Normally he would resent anther week of afternoon shift. Preston was a tough sub-district but with a well-run station commanded by a firm but fair couple of senior sergeants and twelve sergeants. In the old days sergeants could sit on their bums behind desks and leave the work to the baggy-arsed constables on the street . . . but not any more, and certainly not at Preston. Each sergeant took his turn on the van or section car on the hated night or afternoon shifts.

But today Ken was, inexplicably, relaxed and content.

Perhaps it was the drive to work through the mellow, mid-afternoon sunshine of late Autumn – the only season when Melbourne could be described, by anyone but a mindless copywriter for the Tourist Bureau, as 'beautiful'. The pelicans lazed sleepily in the little lagoon beside the freeway, a mile or so before it terminates in the bustling clamour of Hoddle Street. Those old English trees in the park near Carringbush swimming pool were a glowing profusion of gold, warm orange and brown.

Perhaps it was the fact that it was Monday – a predictably quiet evening on the section car.

He checked the roster on the fly-spotted notice board and frowned. Odd. His allocated partner was to be Moose, the brash kid who had been posted to Preston earlier in the year, fresh from the Recruit Academy and eight months on a training station. God knows what the senior sergeant is up to, Ken thought, in rostering us together after that painful night shift which had ended in a punch-up between them.

117

He stirred his coffee reflectively and pondered memories of that night of a month ago. It had been a bastard of a shift. Moose had strode into the mess room beaming. 'Great night for buck-hunting, Sarge!' Ken had glared at him. Sure, Saturday night shifts were usually characterised by battles with the bucks – the drunken, swaggering kids with their over-powered cars – but Ken hated Moose's cowboys-and-Indians enthusiasm. He had wanted to snap back that their job was to maintain the peace, not to collect scalps. Instead he simply muttered: 'Let's hope to Christ it's a quiet one'.

It had in fact turned out to be a quiet shift – a minor pub brawl, a couple of traffic matters and a domestic – but, by five a.m. Ken was tired, his sinuses clogged and his neck muscles stiff from driving. Moose had fidgeted in the passenger seat of the patrolling car.

'Hold it, Sarge! Do a U-turn.'

'Why?'

'There's a bloke pissing in the gutter. We could get him on Wilful and Obscene Exposure under the *Summary Offences Act*.'

Ken's foot did not ease on the accelerator. If anything, it slightly increased the pressure. He had noted, with trained eye, the middle-aged drunk on the pavement as they had cruised past.

'So there is some pathetic little bastard on his way home from a party who can't control his bladder. So what?'

'Well, OK,' said Moose, missing the point, 'it might not be *wilful* exposure but we could nail him on Offensive Behaviour.'

'For being offensive to the hundreds of little old ladies who are walking their dogs in High-bloody-Street Preston at five-fucking-thirty in the morning?' He grated it out, voice rising sharply towards the end.

Moose looked pained.

'Well, yeah, Sarge, it's just that ... well, I mean ... we haven't had an arrest all night.'

Ken flared. 'For chrissake, Moose!' he snapped in a voice louder than he intended, 'Another half-an-hour and the bloody shift will be almost over. And you want to pull in a drunk! You want me to call up the divie van! (And a drunk who is likely to spew goes in the back of the van, not in this bloody sedan, he added, remembering that Moose was new to The Job.) You want me to wake Mad Dog Johnston to sign bail papers! You want . . . you want. . .' Ken tailed off incoherently. He steadied himself and said evenly: 'You want to be able to tell your snot-nosed constable mates that you scored another scalp for your belt. You give me the shits!'

Moose had never heard Ken shout before and he sat in abashed silence.

His silence became truculent muttering when they were changing into civilian clothes in the locker room at seven a.m. and Ken, tired beyond argument, had flattened him with a king hit to the jaw.

Now, a month later, Ken re-checked the roster in the empty mess room and pondered. The kid had, he admitted to himself, responded oddly: reporting for work the next evening, making no comment about the obvious bruise along his jaw bone, and working patiently and doggedly as Ken's partner for the remainder of the week's shift. Mudguts, the aging senior sergeant, knew of the incident but had said nothing. Mudguts prided himself on knowing his troops well and constructing the roster carefully. Perhaps this week's roster, Ken thought, expressed some obscure intuition by the old bastard that the two of them might make a good section car team.

Moose arrived and made the ritual cup of instant coffee. He sat opposite Ken, chatting cheerfully about his new girlfriend and betraying no obvious awkwardness about it being their first shift together since that shift of a month ago when Ken had hit him.

Without waiting for any request from Ken, he finished his coffee and did the routine check on the car. They loaded the gear aboard and headed off.

It was another quiet one. At about four they did an uneventful 'walk through' of the big pub on the north side of the District. Kids from the local technical college, under the legal age of eighteen, had been drinking there and some months ago the senior sergeant had told a crew to check it out; the kids got the message and now it was only a matter of doing an occasional walk-through every few weeks. It meant strolling through the bar and lounge, exchanging banter with the older students who cheerfully produced drivers licences with date of birth. They sat and chatted with some of them, swapping yarns.

At about four-thirty the radio instructed them to return to the station. There, the Duty Senior Sergeant explained that a middle-aged gentleman had come in asking for help; apparently he had accompanied his adult son to the bus stop at the nearby shopping mall for the son to return to the psychiatric hospital after a day's leave with his family. The son had become agitated and refused to leave. The senior sergeant had suggested that the gentleman go back to the son and that police would rendezvous with him there.

It was only a few hundred metres' drive and, as Ken parked the car, the father came over and introduced himself. Ken assessed the situation silently. The son lounged in a shop doorway. He looked to be a gentle bloke, mid to late thirties, with mild facial asymmetry and an indefinably odd manner. He might have been emotionally disturbed but was certainly not intellectually handicapped: he spoke firmly and coherently.

'No, I'm not going back. It's my life, not theirs. I'm not going back for quids.'

Ken remonstrated with him gently.

'No,' he said, 'it's my life. Do you think I am an idiot or something? I've got money in the bank and can look after myself.'

Ken gave reassurance that no-one could force him to do anything. From the side of his mouth he murmured to Moose: 'Two hundred'. Without disturbing the conversation, Moose silently edged away and slipped into the car. The phrase 'Two hundred' is the standard radio call sign of a divisional van. He lifted the microphone and softly requested back-up from the Preston van.

The father hung around ineffectually but then the mother appeared. She was an ugly little woman with an absurdly elaborate hair-do.

'He's schizophrenic, you know!' she snapped, 'They wouldn't put him there without a reason.'

'Bullshit,' the son replied, 'I've been there four years now. Do you think I am an idiot?'

There was an hiatus in the confused discussion and the son blurted out to his mother: 'Can't you put me up for the night?'

'No, we haven't got a bed.'

'But you must have a bed.'

'Yes, and remember what happened last time? You set fire to the house.'

'That was an accident. Can't you put me up overnight?'

'No.'

Meanwhile Ken tried to give reassurance. 'Yes, of course, it is your life: no-one can tell you what to do.' He glanced at Moose with arched eyebrows, non-vocally signalling: 'Where the hell is the divisional van?'

At about that point the van slid in beside them and two constables emerged and took the son by both elbows.

'But it's my life, it's none of your business!'

His mother turned to Moose: 'He's just not trying. It's not that he is mental – just schizophrenic.'

The son realised what the constables were doing and glared at Ken. Moose noted the despairing expression of betrayal on his face. Fatalistically he climbed into the back of the van and sat on the floor mumbling: 'My life . . . my life'. The double doors on the back of the van were swung shut and padlocked. Ken and Moose resumed patrol.

Twenty minutes later there was a minor Code #12: a brewery truck had collided with an early-model sedan driven by an elderly gentleman who spoke little English. Damage to the vehicles was minimal but the truck driver, conscious of the brewery's policy on insurance, had insisted that police be called. Ken stood in the background allowing Moose to handle the confused shouting match. Moose firmly insisted that the truck driver lower his voice; he explained to the other driver his legal rights and ensured that both exchanged names and addresses. Finally, Moose presented the elderly man with a card which, in several languages, gave the addresses of Community Legal Centres where free legal advice would be available. Ken was familiar with the card which was, as far as he could recall, printed in Greek, Italian and Arabic. Ken had worked in the sub-district for some years and could pick that the old man was speaking Turkish but he said nothing: Moose was handling it with amateurish compassion and the Legal Centre would eventually sort it all out.

They took a break at six-thirty and munched their way through hamburgers at the local shop, gossiping quietly. Ken explained to Moose about the Chief Commissioner's doomed attempts to stop members eating there and taking the half-price discount which McDonalds offered to uniformed police members as a public relations gesture. 'Perhaps he's tasted the bloody things', Moose said with a shy grin and Ken chuckled.

At about seven they were on the northern edge of 'Q' District. It was a routine back-up to the div van manned by Stork Phelan and his partner and, when the usual 'Cancel back-up' call came through from VKC, they did a U-turn and cruised slowly south, back down Plenty Road. The sun had almost set and there was the smoky haze of an autumn evening. The flowers in the gardens around the Bundoora hospital glowed with an unnatural intensity. The air was warm and occasionally they caught the gentle smell of burning leaves as householders raked front gardens. Ken lit a cigarette and asked Moose to tell him more about the girlfriend.

Conversation was drowned by the sudden roar of a high-revving motor as a late-model sedan abruptly swung out from behind them and hurtled past. 'Christ, you're a bit cheeky, mate', Ken muttered as he stubbed out his cigarette and flicked on the revolving blue light.

Traffic was light and Ken had no difficulty in locking-in behind him, trusting that he would note their presence and pull over. If anything, the speed of the sedan increased. Moose leaned over and switched on the siren and Ken settled into serious driving. They were getting closer to the city and traffic in the opposite direction was getting thicker.

After about a kilometre they had two clear lanes and Ken eased the car in beside him, travelling parallel. The driver was a long-haired kid of about seventeen. Eventually conscious of the wailing siren, he turned his face slowly towards them. The glazed eyes and blank expression indicated that he was either high on drugs or drunk out of his mind. With the two vehicles running parallel, his eyes met those of Moose, no more than a metre from his, and seemed to dumbly register the reality of the blue uniform. His hesitation was momentary: he flattened the accelerator to the boards and hurtled ahead, leaving them with the vision of the rear of a sedan weaving dangerously through the traffic.

Now it was serious. Ken and Moose slipped instinctively into the routine of a crew handling a fast-moving, and potentially lethal, situation. Ken concentrated on determined driving while Moose alerted VKC that they were 'in pursuit mode' and called for a check on the sedan's number plates. He had the information he needed within eight seconds and shouted above the wail of the siren and the roar of the motor: 'Looks bad, Sarge – it went onto the Stolen Motor Vehicles Register about two hours ago'.

The car swung sharply into Tyler Street. Here, there was virtually no traffic and Ken could accelerate and get in close behind him. With relief, they watched him at last give up and slow to walking pace.

Ken pulled alongside. Simultaneously the driver spat some obscenity which was lost in the howl of the engine as he accelerated violently, scraping paint off the police car with a crumpling mudguard as the car rocketed forward.

Ken settled in behind him. Now the car was swaying across the road like a willow tree in high wind, tyres lurching over the kerb with obscene squeals.

Ken murmured: 'Emergency call'.

Moose understood and gave the call to VKC. The VKC operator, in turn, gave the flat command to all units on Channel Six to 'stand by' and hold off routine signals until a 'hot one' on this channel was cleared. All were aware that the greatest risk of death for a working copper is not in shoot-outs but in high-speed chases.

Although strapped immobile by safety belts in the seat of the car, they worked with the intricate interaction of the ruck and rover of a well-trained Australian-rules football team in the closing quarter. At each intersection Ken would scan right and Moose left, and Moose would murmur: 'Clear left'. Ken manoeuvred the vehicle through corners, expertly aware of the speed at which these unstable sedans would roll, while Moose relayed minute-by-minute data on their location to VKC.

The radio babbled. Preston CIB were setting up a road block at the Murray Street intersection; a Traffic Operations Group (TOG) unit was tailing them – they could even hear, through the crackle of the radio and the wail of their siren, the yelping of the 'yippie' siren used by the TOG sedan about a hundred metres behind them; an unmarked Bureau of Crime Intelligence car, on a totally different job but using the same radio frequency, was swinging west to cut him off at Gower Street.

Moose winced, and momentarily lost the thread of the message he was radioing, as Ken strained the sedan through a barely controlled rear wheel slide into a narrow residential street off Albert Street.

It resolved itself there. They caught a glimpse of the flashing blue light of a car parked as a roadblock some three hundred metres ahead and it was obvious that the idiot in the stolen vehicle had seen it too. He made a couple of frantic attempts at backing and turning in the narrow street and Ken slammed the police car in across the other car with a shrill grating of metal. 'Fuck the grizzles from the senior sergeant at the workshops', Ken muttered. 'This car has already lost a fair bit of paint and the clown is going to kill himself soon.'

They left him in the cells at Preston for a couple of hours to sober up and then, aware that the shift would be over at eleven, did the usual Record of Interview. By this time the kid was relatively sober but his hands still shook visibly. Deliberately, Ken let Moose do the actual questioning and typing.

After the kid had signed the record of interview he relaxed a little and accepted a cup of coffee. He had blown .179% on the breathalyser check. 'Thank Christ you picked me up', he mumbled. 'I might have killed myself!'

Ken had been determined to leave the interrogation to Moose but could not restrain himself from leaning over the desk and snapping: 'And that might have been a good thing, you little cunt! All we were concerned about was that you might have killed some other poor bastard'. Moose completed the paper-work and returned him to the cells.

They changed into civilian clothes and went to the nearby pub which had a late licence and a quiet back room which was always available to a couple of favoured sergeants from Preston station. Moose was conscious that it was unusual for his sergeant to invite him for a beer at the end of an afternoon shift.

They did not discuss the night's work, just yarned about the football. Ken made no comment about Moose's performance but his approval was inherent in the relaxed gossip. Moose grew several years in dignity with the dawning awareness that they had handled a tricky situation as a professional team.

The senior sergeant's perception had been correct: they would make a good crew.

20

SANGUMA

*The personal tragedies which emerge in stark relief
under the spotlight of criminal court proceedings vary
widely in range and depth; in Papua New Guinea
many of the tragedies which are the most poignant and
puzzling – at least to a parochial, white-skinned
Australian such as myself – are interwoven with the
reality of witchcraft and pay-back killings. I have
sometimes shared with colleagues my observation of a
murder trial in 1972 which involved a killer who
hacked to death two ten-year-old boys whom he did not
know personally and who never doubted for a minute
that he was acting honourably. He pleaded guilty to a
charge carrying a maximum penalty of death by
hanging. I intended to describe the court proceedings in
'short story' format to form a chapter of this book and I
unearthed my initial field-diary notes to check details.
Now, as I re-read the slightly-faded notes typed in
Papua New Guinea, I sense that it is somehow
improper to 'tamper' with them. They were written on
the spot. Instead, I will transcribe them verbatim,
leaving to readers to make what they will of this liturgy
of death.*

THE QUEEN VERSUS MAREMEI KUSINA: EXTRACT FROM FIELD NOTES.

BACKGROUND IMPRESSIONS

Source: diary written up in the evening of the first day in Goroka.

After the last Court Circuit in the alpine isolation of Simbai, Goroka is a bustling little metropolis – the administrative centre of the Eastern Highlands District. We arrived by twin-engined Cessna at about one p.m. and were met by the Assistant District Commissioner and an Inspector from the Royal Papua New Guinea Constabulary. After a month on the outstations one is impressed, and initially terrified, by the amount of road traffic: heavy trucks rumbling in from the Highlands Highway, the public mini-buses darting through the main street and, at this time of year, dozens of trucks overflowing with villagers dressed up in the traditional *singsing* finery on their way to the Annual Show.

The court house is a simple, practical building of fibrolite and louvred glass, surrounded by an ill-planned clutter of Administration buildings – District Labour Office, Land Titles Commission, Welfare Department and others.

Tomorrow the Supreme Court will sit in the small courtroom at the rear of the building. Through the thin walls you can hear the District Court in session with the Resident Magistrate conducting proceedings in rapid Tok Pisin while simultaneously taking down a translation into English on the rickety typewriter perched on the Magistrate's bench.

FORMAL DETAILS

Source: Supreme Court file #94/72.

Supreme Court of Papua New Guinea.
Queen v Maremei Kusina.
Wilful murder – two counts.
Coram: Mr Justice Raine.

SUMMARY OF OFFENCE

Source: record of evidence given at the Committal for Trial proceedings.

Maremei is married with three children. In September 1970 his wife died suddenly – apparently as a result of 'sanguma'.[6] No police investigation was conducted and it is now too late to exhume the body but it has all the signs of a classic sanguma killing: she awoke after being rendered unconscious by an unknown assailant and died four days later with the symptoms of peritonitis. There is a real possibility that it was, in Western terms, straightforward murder.

Twelve months later Maremei and a friend went to the nearby village of the man whom his wife had named on her death bed as the sorcerer. They were unable to find him but did find his ten-year-old son, and a same-age playmate, playing in the bush. He beat them both to death with an axe.

On the path leading to where the bodies lay they erected a stick about three feet long (Exhibit D) decorated with leaves and carefully torn strips of newspaper – the symbol that a sorcery killing had been avenged.

---

6   Spelling of the term fluctuates as the foundations for an orthography of Tok Pisin were established only in 1969 with the publication of Mihalic's translation of the *New Testament*. Methods of sanguma vary between areas and have developed over time. Further, the white-man's understanding of it has developed slowly. The first dictionary of Tok Pisin - Murphy's *The Book of Pidgin English*, 1943, gives:

        SANGGUMA: *n.* The term originally comes from Madang where it was used to describe a species of malign sorcery and also the person gifted with the power of performing it. It was performed by bringing about an apparent mesmerism of the victim by the sorcerer who then led him to his assistants and then thorns were pushed into parts of the body where it was desired pain or illness would manifest itself and eventually cause the death of the victim. A short thorn was pushed into the tongue causing it to swell so that the victim could not talk and tell the name of the sorcerers. The thorns were dipped in a special secret brew which apparently rendered them poisonous. The victim invariably died. The term has spread to other parts of the Territory to describe similar sorcery where the victim first undergoes mesmerism or hypnotism.

    Mihalic's *Grammar and Dictionary of Neo-Melanesian* in 1957 simply gives: '*sangguma*, secret murder committed by orders from sorcerers'.

Both were arrested shortly after and spent six months in custody awaiting trial. For technical reasons the Crown did not proceed against Maremei's helper and he was discharged.

FORENSIC SCIENCE ASPECTS

Source: evidence given by the Assistant District Commissioner plus my own notes from cases on previous circuits.

Maremei comes from Akematasa village about thirty-nine miles from Kainantu. It is a remote Highlands village, about two hours' walk through the bush from the nearest road, and is in an area which has a bad reputation for the use of 'hired assassins' – sorcerers who will dispose of an enemy for a fee.

The usual method of sanguma in this area is for the assassin to shadow his victim for some days until he can be sure of finding the victim alone – usually in the coffee gardens. He approaches from behind and knocks the victim unconscious with a blow to the back of the neck. A sliver of bamboo is then inserted either at the base of the tongue or *per anum* piercing the rectal canal about three inches up from the rectum. With the arrival of European technology, a sharpened bicycle spoke is often preferred to bamboo. The sliver is expertly manipulated until it punctures the peritoneal wall. It is sometimes first dipped in excreta to ensure that infection is introduced into the peritoneal cavity.

The victim regains consciousness and finds no apparent physical damage, other than slight bruising to the back of the neck. Occasionally the victim's voice box may be rendered useless by skilful 'karate' chops – leaving the person speechless and thus at a disadvantage, in the absence of literacy, in describing what happened – but this was not done to Maremei's wife.

The prognosis for untreated peritonitis is fairly inexorable: the victim dies with agonising stomach cramps in four to five days.

The technique is known only to a small fraternity of professional sorcerers, plus some European anthropologists, plus most members of the field staff of the Department of District Administration. The victim succumbs to either sorcery or peritonitis – depending on your point of view.

COURTROOM IMPRESSIONS

Source: field diary written up as the case proceeded.

Maremei is in his forties, with close-cropped curly hair balding at the temples. He has rather odd eyes with greyish irises which, I am told, is the result of some sort of dietary deficiency. He is barefooted and dressed in unironed shirt and grubby khaki shorts. He has those very attractive blue/black tattoo marks radiating from the edge of each eye – a common decoration in this area. He has rarely left his village and speaks only South Fore dialect: all evidence is translated into Tok Pisin and then into English. He listens to it all with stoic sadness.

STATEMENT OF THE ACCUSED

Source: Magistrates Court file; evidence on oath.

My name is Maremei. My father's name is Kusina. I am a widower with children. My wife is dead. I come from Akematasa village. When my wife got sick – before she died – she called the name of Arawote. She said: 'I am going to die because Arawote has cast a spell on me. Now I am going to die and so you must do a payback for me: go and kill Arawote'.

When my wife died and left our daughter who is not old enough to walk, I looked after her myself and carried her around. I was thinking about what my wife told me about killing Arawote as a payback but I was worrying because my daughter is not old enough yet – if I go to gaol – and so I waited for her to grow up.

My wife died in the ninth month and I buried her near my house. Sometimes I took my daughter and carried her on top of the grave and cried. When my daughter saw me crying she also cried. When I saw my daughter crying I was strongly thinking about going to kill Arawote.

The old mother of mine and two married people – Eta and his wife Lowa – heard my wife say the name of Arawote before she died.

On the Monday I carried my daughter and walked to the grave of my wife. My daughter again cried and I was very sorry for her. That is why, on the Tuesday morning, I left my house and found Maiwina at the Akematasa aid post. I told him: 'You will come and we will find Arawote and kill him for payback for my wife because he killed her'. Maiwina said: 'That is all right, we will go'.

We then left and walked to a valley near where Arawote lived and we looked for him to kill him. We then sat by a small hill and ate some sweet potato. We then went up a creek and came to some palm trees. I took some nuts off the palms. We then walked more and hid in the kunai grass.

Aito and Ero came along.[7] Ero was walking first followed by Aito. I then told Maiwina: 'You must watch out for men'. I then took my axe and walked along the gully to follow the two boys into the garden. I hid myself there. The two boys walked into the garden and then out again. I followed behind. I walked slowly and quietly behind them in case they should see me and run away.

I first got hold of Aito but swung my axe to cut Ero. I got hold of Aito but Ero turned to see me and I struck him on the side of the neck. I swung my axe twice to cut Ero and he fell down and blood shot out. Some blood fell on me. When Aito saw me cut Ero he sung out saying: 'A man has got hold of me – a murderer!' When I heard him shout I hurried and struck him as well. Before I struck him I pushed him down and held him down with my left hand, holding the axe in my right hand. I then cut through the bone of his neck.

After that I straightened their bodies on the spot where they had been killed. I was frightened that someone would come and I ran away, following the fence of the garden. I sang out to Maiwina and he came down to me. Maiwina said: 'Did you kill him?' I told him I had killed two men. We tied the small grasses to the tree to show Arawote that I had done a payback.

We hid in the bush until it was dark and then went home. We came to Okai's house – the medical aid post – and found three

---

7   Notes from the police file are ambiguous. It would seem that Maremei only learnt the names of the boys through police questioning but it does seem that he knew that one of them was a son of Arawote. Within the strict rules of the payback tradition it was sufficient for him that he knew, from the fact that they were in that particular coffee garden, that they were members of Arawote's clan.

boys around a fire. I sat down with them and warmed myself and then left and went to my mother's house and slept. The next morning I went to my garden and planted taro. I heard that people were looking for the two boys Aito and Ero. I did not say anything because I knew that nobody had seen me. I just sat quiet.

After that I heard that the two boys had been found. Some men from my village went to see the bodies. I did not go: I stayed in my house. On Saturday the people carried the two dead bodies to meet the police and the doctor. After the doctor finished examining the bodies he left and the police came to the village. I was thinking whether to admit or deny. The police slept in the village that night but I did not tell them.

At daybreak a police corporal and an interpreter asked me to walk with them. We went some distance from the village. We sat down and the corporal said: 'Is there a track or footpath in that area of bush?' He pointed to the place where I had walked to kill the two boys. I said: 'No, there is not a track through that area'. The corporal said: 'I dreamt a dream last night. You were pulling bird-of-paradise feathers out of the kunai and waving them at us'.

I said to the corporal: 'You are right to see me. I am the man who killed the two boys'. The corporal stopped me and told me not to tell him. He said: 'It is all right for you not to tell me. That is something belonging to you. If you wish to talk out loud, you may do so but if you wish to shut your mouth you may do so. If you wish to talk about when you killed the two boys you may do so'.

I said to the corporal: 'I am the man who killed the two boys'.

DISPOSITION

Source: Supreme Court Register

Guilty on two counts of wilful murder. Sentenced to imprisonment with hard labour for five years and six months on the first and six years on the second, to be served concurrently.

21

OFFICERS MESS

He sometimes stumbles out of bed, fumbling to kill the shrilling alarm clock and trying to come to terms with the aching reality of yet another hangover . . . and momentarily recalls a fleeting dream, buried somewhere in the sluggish night's sleep, of a moment of gentleness and directness, perhaps even of love. Such moments come, are glimpsed, and dissipate.

It is in some such fashion that he remembers Herself Robinson.

She was tall – formidably tall – with blond hair which swept down to her hips. She did not smile: she grinned broadly – the open, direct expression of her interaction with her colleagues. The cheekbones were high and angular in a symmetrical, triangular face like a Chinese lady. She was gently gleeful.

*   *   *   *

In 1965 the criminal justice system of the Northern Territory was raw and rickety. The Prisons Service consisted of little more than the rusty, galvanised-iron building known as 'Fanny Bay Gaol'. The local joke was that it was the only prison in the southern hemisphere from which you could escape with the aid of a can-opener. In the absence of any adult probation and parole service, the judges and magistrates had only the options of awarding convicted offenders an unsupervised bond, a fine, a short spell in Fanny Bay or a free aeroplane flight to Adelaide to serve long sentences in 'Yatala', South Australia's maximum security prison.

The Director of Social Welfare recruited him in Melbourne with the offer of a position as 'Senior Social Worker' and a mandate to do the preliminary planning for the establishment of a probation and parole service. It was an exciting challenge and he accepted eagerly. In fact, when he got there, he found himself with the responsibility of coordinating many of the family welfare services which the Northern Territory Administration offered in Darwin – a task for which he had few skills – but, whenever time allowed, he worked doggedly on research into probation and parole systems. At government expense he visited the probation and parole services of other States of the Commonwealth and had visions of an advanced service, designed with an appreciation of the strengths and weakness of those of the other States, which would develop within the Welfare Branch of the Northern Territory Administration.

He was naive about power politics. It took him some time to realise that the major obstacle to the project was tension between the Commonwealth Attorney-General's Department based in Canberra and the Northern Territory Administration based in Darwin. Each wanted to have control of any new bureaucratic development. Put more negatively, each was preoccupied with preventing the other from having control. They quibbled. One year became two and two years became three. The utter inability of the existing criminal justice system to deal with violent offenders was a disaster waiting to happen. At times he found himself secretly wishing that someone personifying inviolate sanctity – preferably Mother Teresa or at least the grandmother of a prominent politician – would be raped and murdered in the main street of Darwin by some desperately frustrated escapee from Fanny Bay Gaol. The press would galvanise public outrage and the bureaucrats might finally be goaded into getting on with the job.

No such symbolic 'little old lady', nor any hypothetical homicidal rapist, ever appeared and three years became four. He did his work in the family welfare agency as best he could but he hankered for the criminal justice industry which was his real trade. Some colleagues in the security services and the police force had links with the Army Reserve and, along with two ASIO agents, he enlisted for part-time officer training, graduating as a second lieutenant with the local anti-aircraft unit. His skills at running a family welfare agency were on a par with his skills as an artillery subaltern: he was arguably the most inept junior officer ever foisted upon the Australian Army.

Four years became five and he was drinking heavily. With understandable despair his wife left him, taking the car, the kids and the cat and moving to Melbourne. At about the same time word came through that Federal Parliament had passed amendments to the legislation allowing for adult probation and parole in the Northern Territory. The service would be administered by the Commonwealth Attorney-General's Department. They had won. Plans for a locally based outfit evaporated.

If one thinks like an accountant, it shouldn't have worried him. He had a good salary and the security of tenure as a public servant complete with superannuation, long service leave and all that. But somehow it all seemed a bit pointless. He took a stretch of unused recreation leave and flew to Papua New Guinea, booked into a boarding house and sat around the Port Moresby RSL Club pondering where he could go from here.

As an unofficial network of support and contact, the Army Reserve can sometimes be akin to freemasonry. Within the first few days of wandering around Moresby he bumped into a lawyer who had been a reservist with the Darwin unit and they shared gossip which was in turn relayed to colleagues. A few days later he was invited for drinks at the Supreme Court. It seemed that Mr Justice Raine had served as an anti-aircraft sergeant during World War II and, after demobilisation in 1945, had maintained his links with the Army by joining the Reserve. He was now a colonel and, although a part-timer, he technically outranked the lieutenant colonel who was Officer Commanding Papua New Guinea Defence Forces. But the folklore of the Artillery Corps has subtle distinctions of caste: at the lowest stratum are the anti-aircraft units, derisively referred to as 'the bird gunners' by the Field Artillery. The judge had expressed interest on hearing that there was another 'bird gunner' visiting Moresby.

He was a charming, crusty old bachelor. He had, he explained, only recently been elevated to the Bench of the

Supreme Court of Papua New Guinea and had not as yet appointed an 'associate': a mixture of private secretary and bodyguard or, in military terms, an 'aide-de-camp' or 'subaltern staff officer'. As they chatted they both tacitly realised that the relationship between a Justice of the Supreme Court and his associate was pretty much analogous to that between a colonel and a subaltern. After some further meetings an agreement was reached and he flew back to Darwin to seek a transfer from the Northern Territory Administration.

The Director of Social Welfare was less than helpful. The Northern Territory Administration would not consider a transfer until they had consulted with the Papua New Guinea public service and the Commonwealth public service. The bureaucrats had rigid rules about not poaching from each other. He relinquished routine duties and was classified as 'on indeterminate leave without pay'. After two weeks there was a further meeting with the Director in which he tendered his resignation, forgoing all claims to superannuation, seniority and all that, but it was still not acceptable. Memoranda moved sluggishly between the three bureaucracies; three weeks became a month, one month became two and he paced the empty Darwin house.

Herself Robinson was a social worker in the agency where he had worked over those five years in Darwin. They were colleagues and she offered support where she could. He, preoccupied with the waiting, barely noticed the patience with which she would drop in for a cup of coffee after work and listen to his loneliness.

In the third month the papers finally came through: his appointment to the Papua New Guinea Supreme Court was confirmed and he was to catch the Monday flight to Port Moresby.

He did not think of Herself. His first impulse was to break the news to Bill Denton, another friend who had supported him through a rough spell. Denton existed by day as a gung-ho technical officer with the Water Resources Branch and, by night and weekend, as an even more gung-ho artillery Lieutenant with the Army Reserve. It was Denton who had first encouraged him into undergoing training with the Reserve.

The travel papers to Papua New Guinea had arrived on the Friday morning and Friday evening was 'happy hour' at the officers mess: the once-a-week session when all members of the mess, regular or reservist, come together informally after work and etiquette between the ranks is relaxed, the price of beer lowered and plates of cheese, biscuit and sausage placed around the bar.

Happily, he found Denton there. He told him the news. They bought beers and talked excitedly about the Papua New Guinea job. And sentimentally about their years together in Darwin.

They were interrupted by Major Fields, the President of the Mess Committee (PMC).

Within the esoteric folklore of the Army, the PMC exists slightly above the Chiefs of the General Staff and a little below God: you politely greet him on entering the mess, listen respectfully to his chit-chat as he does the rounds of the groups of drinking officers, and never, never, leave the mess without first asking his permission. He is a symbol somewhat like the Queen in a summons issued by a criminal court: 'Her Majesty the Queen commands that you, Blurtbum Muxworthy, do attend Darwin Magistrates Court at ten in the forenoon to answer the charge that you did unlawfully, wilfully and with malice aforethought wave your poxy old dong at a passing schoolgirl. . .' The figurehead is the keystone of the ritual – even if Elizabeth II may be engrossed in breeding corgies and perhaps uninterested in, or even unaware of, the existence of the local Darwin flasher.

So with the PMC. You address him with deference, obey his whims and buy him drinks, knowing instinctively that the liturgy of the mess revolves around his symbolic authority. The personality behind the symbol should not matter.

But, in that particular year, the incumbent of the position was a pain in the arse. Major Fields, referred to as 'Old WC' by all members, was a shrivelled little man who had been a barracks officer for some years, slipping inexorably into futile alcoholism with the unintentioned aid of a bitchy wife who insisted that he should by now be holding the rank of lieutenant colonel if only he had tried harder. He clung to the title 'President of the Mess Committee' shrilly.

'Glad to see you young reservists here for happy hour!' he boomed hollowly. 'The Committee believes that a good military mess is so much more complete with the attendance of officers from . . . er . . . the support units.'

He never bothered to learn the names of the part-time officers and, tonight, could not even recall which units they came from.

They nodded politely.

'And of course you'll be here on Sunday night?'

They gazed at him blankly.

'Good god, man, it's the formal dinner-dance! Everyone will be here with their good ladies!'

'And of course,' he added ominously, '*all* subalterns!'

They nodded weakly and he moved on to the next group.

They sat in silence. Both knew that a junior subaltern had no alternative but to obey. Both knew that these dinner-dances were stilted ceremonials for bored officers' wives . . . and for equally bored senior officers who liked to look over the junior officers' wives.

'I'm sorry, mate,' Denton murmured, 'that'll be your last night in Darwin, won't it?'

He nodded glumly.

'Aw, come on, mate!' Denton said, 'It could be worse: we can still sink a few beers together before you go and there'll be mobs of tucker.'

Then Denton paused and frowned. 'Aw, shit! It's just dawned on me: it's a formal *Ladies'* Night. You'll be expected to front up to the PMC and all the senior officers and introduce your wife. Fuck! Look, we can't get out of this bullshit now. Why don't you phone Herself Robinson: she might help and play the part?'

He did, the next day. He outlined the problem. She said: 'OK' with a cheerful simplicity which rendered redundant any further apologies or explanation.

He, awkward in hired dinner suit, picked her up at her flat on the Sunday night. She wore an ankle-length dress of some folk-weave stuff which was split, Asian style, to her thigh.

She chuckled at the tatty splendour of the uniformed guards on the porch of the officers mess and the two ceremonial searchlights on either side which shafted meaninglessly up into the Darwin night sky.

The ballroom was crowded. They danced.

Within the loneliness and fixedness of the aftermath of a busted marriage his mind had registered her presence only as that of a patient and unobtrusive friend: it had never occurred to him to think of her sexually. Abruptly he realised that she was a very beautiful woman who moved with an easy sensuality. She had been, he remembered, a jazz ballet dancer before coming to Darwin. He found himself gazing.

'Oh, come on, you uptight old bastard, relax!' she chuckled, 'You dance well. Just slip into the rhythm and move with it!'

He did, vaguely conscious that a number of eyes were turned upon him and his tall, graceful partner.

At the next bracket of music a captain from the Infantry invited her to dance.

At the following bracket it was a Major from the Artillery.

He lit a cigarette and gazed at the noisy, joyless room. Clearly Herself had become something of a focus of attention. Many of the men there were the worn, restless cogs of 'the Green Machine' – the Regular Army. Many of the women were the brittle, perfumed husks of life as 'officers' wives' in the bitchy desert of the barracks. One set watched with leering interest, the other with catty contempt but most seemed conscious of the presence of Herself.

'Ah, Lieutenant! You could hardly refuse the fraternal plea of a fellow officer for permission to dance with your charming, so charming, wife!'

As the pompous prick wore the epaulettes of a lieutenant colonel on his mess jacket, he could, indeed, hardly refuse. Herself Robinson grinned gently at him and, with her eyes, signalled:

'Relax! Just slip into the rhythm and move with it. I'll be back!' She followed the colonel onto the dance floor.

He ambled over to the bar. Ozzie greeted him and, without waiting to be asked, poured him a beer.

Ozzie and Phil were the two regular Army privates allocated to the permanent posting of 'Bar Steward, Officers Mess, Northern Territory Command'. They handled their unheroic vocation with cheerful competence: pilfering massive amounts of alcohol and cigarettes from the mess, skilfully evading the more tiresome demands of the officers and living rather well while presenting a carefully controlled servility to the idiots who claimed a god-given role as their superiors.

He knew and respected them both. They had a canny appraisal of the pecking order of an officers mess, aware that a subaltern was the lowest rank of the officer caste and that a *reservist* subaltern – who had gained his commission by a mickey-mouse course of part-time study – was beyond the pale. It created a bond between them and, within the coyly stilted language of private-to-officer dialogue, they had shared many happy hours of yarning on quiet nights when the mess was almost deserted.

'Jesus, Sir, the bird's a bloody ripper! Where did you find a bit of fanny like that?'

'None of your business, Steward! She's a good friend. Anyway, I can't get near her: every bastard wants to dance with her.'

'Yeah, story of my life too, Sir.'

Denton emerged from the throng and sank onto the adjoining bar stool. 'I'm stuck with the CO and his brainless bloody wife. But hang cool, mate, the show will be over soon and we'll get a chance to yarn.'

He rose to leave but the music stopped and Herself joined them. She embraced them both with a murmured apology. Without being asked, Ozzie mixed a gin and tonic having noted, with a professional bar tender's skill, her preference in drinks.

He introduced her to Ozzie and more beers were poured all round.

'Christ,' she whispered 'they're a bunch of bores! Every one of them seems to think that he's John Travolta and expects me to gush about his macho seductiveness while he's trampling over my fucking feet! I'm sorry: have I made a mess of your evening?'

'Jesus, no! You've been bloody marvellous.'

'OK,' she said softly, 'it's just that ... well, it's your last night in Darwin and ... well, I just want you to be ...' She abandoned verbalisation and simply grinned with that open gentleness.

He wanted to touch her hand and even stirred to do so but an officer loomed up and bowed stiffly. She rose and glanced back at the three of them. Ozzie beckoned, leaned over the bar and whispered to her: 'Don't worry, Ma'am: they'll all piss off soon'.

They did indeed. At midnight the band disbanded, trundling out guitars and amplifiers like ambulance attendants silently clearing the scene of another fatal accident. The PMC instructed Phil to get the radiogram going. Denton despatched his wife home in a taxi with a patent lie about being obliged to stay behind on regimental business. Other couples danced lethargically to the recorded music.

At one a.m. most of them stumbled out the door with wives nosing among the moving flock like sheep dogs.

By two a.m. the few remaining raucous groups of drinkers had fragmented into isolated drunken individuals.

At two-fifteen Ozzie slammed the door on the last straggler with finality.

Phil switched off all the lights but one over the bar and one over the dance floor. Ozzie selected an old Mersey-side record and turned up the volume on the record player. Phil poured beers for the four of them and a gin and tonic for Herself.

They danced. Herself was gleefully tireless, dancing with each of them in turn. She chuckled over Denton's exaggerated anecdotes. She winced benignly as Phil demonstrated a dance routine he had learnt in Borneo during the Malaya Emergency. She giggled as Ozzie, expertly mimicking the voice of the PMC proposing a toast, nominated Phil as 'Paraplegic of the Year on the Dance Floor'.

Phil rummaged through the bar cupboards and produced a cardboard carton of old disks discarded by the Entertainment Committee of the Mess and salvaged by Ozzie. There were old 45 r.p.m. recordings of Chuck Berry, dozens of long-play disks of syrupy Hollywood stuff and even two brittle 78 r.p.m. records of Dixieland jazz. They riffled through them, sharing memories of the way in which particular songs are linked in fluid memory with particular moments of intense awareness during the lurching, step-by-step business of growing.

A buzzer sounded with the intrusiveness of a dentist's drill. It was about three a.m. 'Aw, shit!' Ozzie muttered, 'That'll be either the Military Police or else that fuck-witted President of the Mess Committee.'

The other three males grunted apprehension. All knew of the PMC's proclivity for waking up with a thirst in the early hours, ringing the doorbell of the mess and imperiously demanding that the stewards get out of bed and fetch him a drink.

Their premonition was accurate.

'My god, how kind of you to stay up for me! Yes, Steward, I will indeed have a beer. The ten ounce glass, thank you. And my dear ... er ...Subaltern, I am delighted that you and your charming wife are still here. She does, if I may say so without offence, dance superbly. May we, Madam? And Steward, would you turn off that dreadful modern music and put on something suitable.'

Phil stoically skewered a Mantovani record on to the turntable. Herself shrugged cheerfully, winked and followed the Major on to the dance floor. Ozzie whispered: 'Relax, Sir, just slip into the rhythm and move with it. He won't be here long'.

Mantovani eventually faded into the sunset and the PMC returned to the bar sweating and beaming. 'Magnificent!' he said, 'Magnificent! A drink for the lady, Steward!' He was swaying slightly.

Ozzie mixed a gin and tonic and handed it to Herself. He turned back to the shelves behind the bar, selected a ten ounce glass, polished it and filled a third of it with vodka.

'And a beer for me, Steward!'

Ozzie nodded respectfully, topped up the glass of vodka with frothy beer and slid it across to the Major.

The PMC drained it and escorted Herself back to the dance floor. With the detachment of a hospital pharmacist, Ozzie prepared another beer glass with tasteless, colourless vodka, this time half full.

The music ended. 'Excellent, excellent!' mumbled the Major, awkwardly organising his arse on to a bar stool. Ozzie, with the professional bar tender's skill at anticipating the needs of his patron, topped up the glass with beer and handed it to the PMC without waiting to be asked.

The PMC sipped and rambled. Herself Robinson listened with patience. The two subalterns watched like frozen rabbits. The bar stewards waited quietly.

The Major emptied the glass, slid it across the bar for a re-fill and lurched to his feet. 'Your wife, Sir, is . . . I must say, Sir, is . . . is . . .' He teetered for a moment and then moved with the simplicity of one of those newsreel shots of a tall brick chimney being demolished by explosives: a graceful curving motion downwards, ending in a cluttering rumble as his face and other front parts flattened into the floor.

'Do excuse us, Ma'am', said Ozzie.

The two stewards stepped from behind the bar with the resigned professionalism of neurosurgeons undertaking yet another lobotomy. Phil took the ankles and Ozzie lifted by the shoulders. They trooped across the cavernous dance floor, their burden horizontal and face downwards, one limp hand dragging on the polished floor. They manoeuvred him through the door and laid him on the lawn beneath a Casuarina tree.

Phil re-locked the door. Ozzie changed the disk on the record player and adjusted the volume. Phil poured beers and made another gin and tonic for Herself, adding a slice of lemon and some chopped mint leaves which they kept in the fridge for special friends.

They danced.

Somewhere around day-break he touched her hand. Gently.

22

PLEA IN MITIGATION OF SENTENCE

Like any prison, Barwon River Reafforestation Camp has a distinct social structure quite independent of the 'man-management' charts pinned to the wall of the Governor's office. The day-to-day functioning of the prison rests on a set of power relationships. In a symbiotic relationship with the guards, the 'heavies' – the hardened long-term prisoners – rule the younger, vulnerable prisoners serving short sentences. Thus are roles allocated to individual prisoners within a complex economy of the distribution of power and privilege.

The 'class conflict' dichotomies of the social hierarchy are rather more stark at Barwon River than at other prisons because it is a minimum-security institution. Most of the prisoners are regarded by the authorities as 'one off' offenders, not committed to a career of crime, who can be trusted not to escape from the wall-less camp. The other group are violent career criminals who have served extremely long sentences; the policy is to allow them to serve the last part in a minimum-security facility, assuming that they will pose no problem as they are anticipating imminent release on parole. It makes for a very rigid social structure in which one is either one of the rulers or one of the ruled.

But, as in any social structure, there were always a few singular human beings who were isolated, slotting into no category of caste. Kim was certainly a 'one off' offender. He had pursued a career as a hard-working, rather idealistic young lawyer but, at fifty years of age, had found himself the scapegoat for a Taxation Department swoop on barristers understating their taxable income. He was skinny with a boyish face. His most obvious characteristic was his taciturn gentleness. He interacted as best he could with the other first-timers but his university education, and concealed love for poetry and music, formed an intangible barrier to acceptance by the knockabout blokes doing short terms for assault and drink-driving, and he was something of an isolate.

Lizard was also socially unslottable. A chunky New Zealander in his fifties, he talked with the other first-timers with politely grave reticence. Appropriately, he was given the job of 'mess hall billet': the solitary caretaker of the mess hall, sweeping the floor, wiping down tables, filling salt shakers. He performed the role with quiet professionalism.

It was there that Kim first got to know Lizard. Kim was 'doing his time hard', desperately missing his wife and kids and overwhelmed by the grey, bland brutality of prison life. After the day's work he tended to dawdle over the evening meal, often ending up peering silently into a mug of tea, alone in the cavernous mess hall occupied only by him and by Lizard methodically wiping tables. Birds sometimes found their way into the unlined, ceiling-less hall and perched on the rafters and on one such occasion Kim became aware of a tiny honeyeater peering quizzically down at him. It was exquisite. Its feathers like crafted filigree, orange tips subtly melding into gold and burnt sienna. It was poetry, it was music, a re-affirmation of beauty transforming the squalor of prison. Kim was transfixed in wonderment. 'My god,' he whispered, 'just look at that.'

Lizard glanced up. 'Nah. It wouldn't be worth more than ten or fifteen dollars.'

The moment was lost. Kim's reverie dissolved into consciousness of the drabness of the mess hall and its raw, bland concrete floor. Lizard's mind vaguely registered the draining despair on the other's face and he mumbled an apology, explaining that he was a wildlife smuggler who liked to keep his mind on his job.

In subsequent evenings of conversation in the deserted mess hall Kim came to gradually piece together some understanding of his strange fellow-prisoner. Lizard's prison nickname had nothing to do with his appearance but with his expertise in handling birds and reptiles. He and his wife and children lived in a modest but comfortable home in New Zealand where he spent all his time as a concerned father and husband, leaving only for the occasional international trips which constituted his bread-winning activities. Over several decades he had built up contacts with the middle-men who supplied the lucrative market for exotic birds and animals sought by wealthy owners of private zoos in California. The syndicate which controlled the multi-million-dollar industry consisted of a clique of ruthless entrepreneurs but Lizard always insisted on working as a freelancer. The syndicate respected his skills and from time to time would indicate specific needs expressed by their clients and Lizard would do the selection, packaging and delivery. It meant flying to exotic countries where he would expertly trap feral birds and reptiles – or, if that were not possible, buy them from the locals – and deliver them to the wealthy dilettantes in San Francisco. The commission he was paid was very high and he lived the life of a globe-trotting businessman, sometimes lingering for a few days in tropical resorts before returning to his loving family. Airline clerks and customs officials rarely troubled him, imagining him to be some sort of elderly Presbyterian bank manager engaged in international commerce.

Kim began to understand a little of Lizard's isolation from the other prisoners. He found it hard, he confessed to Kim, to accept the label 'criminal'. His was an illegal but gentlemanly profession. This was his first gaol term. And he had never, never, stolen anything from anyone nor ever used violence.

One night he inquired as to Kim's profession. Inevitably they ended up discussing the court proceedings which had culminated in Lizard's stay at Barwon River. Kim expressed surprise at the shortness of the sentence for an offence under the *Customs Act* 1901 which carried a severe maximum penalty. 'Christ, you must have had a pretty sharp barrister giving a plea in mitigation of sentence?'

'Well, yes, I suppose you could say that,' Lizard grunted, 'though the plea didn't exactly follow what I had planned.' And he told the story to Kim:

The syndicate indicated that some North American collectors were prepared to pay high money for Australian blue-tongued lizards, parakeets and parrots. Lizard flew from New Zealand to Melbourne, rented a four-wheel-drive vehicle and spent some time on the Dargo High Plains and the Grampians, trapping specimens or buying them from local aviaries. He arrived at Melbourne International Airport with two expertly packed suitcases: one full of lizards, the other of parrots, all carefully fed, sedated and wrapped in cotton wool.

Once the suitcases were checked in, he strolled up to the departure lounge but was accosted by two officers of the Customs Service who asked if they could speak with him about some apparent irregularities in his travel arrangements and visa. Lizard was not alarmed: he had been in this profession for some decades and, unruffled, he replied with polite but distant agreement. In the office, they checked and rechecked their computer. Lizard watched with an expression of severe patience. It turned out to be an utterly trivial computer error: two digits in a visa number had been accidentally transposed, triggering a computer-generated demand for a check by the Customs Service. They apologised profusely. Lizard accepted their apologies with the gravity of a bank manager dealing with a callow teller. They were still embarrassed.

'We're truly sorry, Sir, but, you see, they load us with so many tasks. We're supposed to double check the immigration details, do a personal search for drugs, check your luggage for wildlife smuggling and all that – all because of some stupid clerical error.'

'Quite so, quite so. I fully understand.'

'. . . and we've already held you up for ten minutes. It *is* embarrassing.'

'Think nothing of it! You have a difficult job to do and I will certainly not be lodging any complaint. Besides, on the matter of wildlife in luggage, I can assure you that one of my suitcases is full of parrots and the other is full of lizards.'

They roared with laughter, chuckling with relief at his sensitivity and wry humour. They ushered him to the door and wished him a safe and enjoyable journey.

But the story did not end there. For totally unconnected reasons, it was *not* 'a safe and enjoyable journey': in fact Lizard never got off the ground. Uncharacteristically, he had misjudged the amount of anaesthetic appropriate to one of the larger parrots and some damned baggage-handler, doing the final loading on to the plane, had noted muffled squawking coming from a suitcase. Clearance for take-off was withdrawn and eventually two Australian Federal Police members escorted Lizard from the plane.

After the committal-for-trial proceedings, Lizard gravely considered his options. There was little hope of beating the charges which carried a hefty maximum penalty; 'best practice' was to plead guilty and seek a discounted sentence. Other prisoners in the Remand Centre drew his attention to advertisements in the press from a less-than-reputable law firm which touted for business in any area of law. The barrister they supplied was regarded with some disdain by senior members of the Bar but perhaps secretly admired for his skilful manipulation of judges and magistrates. He and Lizard were both professionals and had an instant mutual respect for each other's roles. Uncharacteristically the secretive Lizard was totally frank as he briefed him on precise details of his lengthy career and of the recent unfortunate incident.

After the routine preliminaries of the County Court, the barrister rose to make a plea in mitigation of sentence. He described his client's stable and deep commitment to his wife and children in New Zealand. He drew attention to the fact that his client had an unblemished record: not one prior conviction – not as much as a parking ticket. He mentioned his client's deep love for birds and animals. Rising to rhetorical cadence, he outlined the evil intrusion by American gangsters who had approached his client with the offer of an enormous amount of money for one delivery of wildlife – enough for his client to see that his children lived comfortably to the end of their days – and, for once in his life, he had succumbed to temptation. In fact he had not received a penny and the wildlife had never left Australia. Overcome with remorse at the enormity of what he had unwittingly become involved in, he had cooperated with police with complete frankness and had insisted on pleading guilty to save the community the expense of empanelling a jury and calling witnesses.

The judge nodded approvingly and indicated that he would substantially reduce the sentence in the light of the remorse and frankness expressed in a plea of guilty.

'Ah, but there is much, much more to my client's frankness and honesty . . .'

Lizard swivelled his eyes towards the barrister with puzzlement.

'. . . much more, Your Honour. You will note that even *before* he was arrested by Federal Police he made frank admissions to two Customs officers. I draw Your Honour's attention to the record of evidence given by one of the Customs officers to the lower court. Page three of the depositions, fourth line from the bottom. He was not under any suspicion by these officers – they spoke to him only in relation to a trivial computer error – yet, overcome with remorse, he blurted out – and I quote verbatim – "One of my suitcases is full of parrots and the other is full of lizards." This, Your Honour, is no ordinary criminal!'

The judge glanced at Lizard with admiration and imposed the lowest possible sentence of imprisonment.

*   *   *   *

'So you see,' said Lizard in the deserted mess hall, 'sharp lawyers can sometimes be useful.'

'Well, yes, I suppose you could say that', murmured Kim. 'I wouldn't know.'

23

PLEA ON
ADMISSIBILITY OF EVIDENCE

Luigi was a proud old patriarch. He had raised four healthy sons, now in their twenties. In forty years of dogged work pushing a barrow and haggling with the customers of his vegetable stall at the Vic' Market he never had time to learn 'Oxford' English. But he could be operatically voluble in the patois of the market.

The sons had prospered – running their own stalls plus a few other business enterprises – but he had been incensed by one particular episode in which the youngest son had been arrested by North Melbourne CIB. It was not the crime – a minor misunderstanding between business competitors – but the fact that the police had cut corners in preparing the prosecution brief. They had verballed. The son had been invited to sign a prepared type-written confession. With the heritage of his father's pride, he had refused and it took four detectives, working in relay, to batter him into providing a semi-conscious signature.

The next morning the patriarch was aghast at his son's dishevelled appearance: two fractured ribs and saliva dribbling from a swollen lip. Four against one! It was a matter of *onerta*.

Against the advice of the family's solicitor, he insisted on attending the Magistrates Court. There, the solicitor routinely challenged the admissibility of the coerced confession as evidence. The old man gabbled to the solicitor who eventually, and very reluctantly, called him as a witness.

In examination-in-chief, the patriarch described his son's honour and, in graphic detail, the injuries which the police had inflicted upon him. His grammar and syntax were often convoluted, his vocabulary occasionally purple, but one could hardly deny the conviction with which he described the dishonourable assault on his son.

In cross-examination, the police prosecutor took him back over each detail of the alleged injuries inflicted. Steadfastly the father repeated what he had said. The prosecutor pointed out that the police station record books contained no evidence of violence being used. The father snorted contemptuously. Finally the prosecutor drew the usual trump card: 'And so, Witness, if these imagined injuries were as serious as you claim, you would, of course, have reported the matter?'

'Whadda you saying?'

'I mean you would have reported your allegations to the authorities, would you not?'

'Report to who?'

'To the police, Witness. If, as seems unlikely, there were any substance to your suspicions that violence might have been used, you, as a citizen, have a perfect right – indeed, perhaps a moral obligation – to complain to the senior officer of your local police station.'

The patriarch gazed with disdain at the young prosecutor. 'You tink I'm a some sort of stupido, huh?' he said evenly, 'You getta your arm chomped offa by some lion. So you go finda some other lion and tell him da story, huh? You giva me da shits, stupido!'

Accounts of people who were present vary. All agree that the magistrate said nothing. Some say they detected a covert, thoughtful smile on the magistrate's face. The written confession was ruled as inadmissible evidence and the son was acquitted.

24

DRUNK AND DISORDERLY

Carl was an embarrassment. No one would state it as baldly as that – in The Job you support your limping mates and say as little as possible – but everyone at the station knew it. It was not that he was corrupt or brutal in the way in which the media often depicts policemen. He was simply a useless member of the team. He was sullen and had no close friends among the station staff. In fact he had very few acquaintances with whom he could chat amiably; his drinking problem meant frequent and unpredictable days off on sick leave which, in turn, meant double shifts and cancelled rest days for everyone else. It was his drinking too which was the basis of most of the other hassles: the outbursts of rudeness to civilians over the watch-house counter, the mislaid paperwork, the unnecessary aggression – usually verbal, sometimes physical – towards the local kids.

He was a senior constable in his mid-thirties – an age when, within the normal career ladder, he could expect to hold the rank of Sergeant. Over-age senior constables are in many ways the backbone of the police force: often the best operational police are the older men who have no desire to battle their way upwards through the study, the exams and the promotion boards, and who are content to remain at that rank until retirement, collecting wisdom and street skills rather than stripes on their shirt. Others, like Carl, may be there as a result of a string of minor disciplinary charges and a chronic inability to learn.

It was this matter of Carl's age and rank which made for a particularly stilted relationship with Pete, one of the six sergeants at the station. They had been through recruit training together, fifteen years before.

Superficially Pete had a cheerful boyish face. Close-up, it was creased with strain and controlled anger. Pete had few ambitions and even fewer illusions about the glamour and challenge of police work. He often dreamed of leaving The Job but sensed that there were few opportunities Outside for someone with no qualifications other than the three useless stripes on his sleeve. He accepted that and worked doggedly at the station with a commitment and professionalism which went unnoticed by his superiors.

This professionalism was occasionally compromised by Carl's blunders. He had no love for Carl but they had been rookie squad members together and he naturally tried to cover for him where he could.

*　　　　*　　　　*　　　　*

At about nine-thirty p.m. the two constables in the divisional van received a 'Dirty Thirty' call over the radio: the routine request to assist a member on foot patrol who had arrested someone as Drunk and Disorderly ('Code #30') who was too inebriated to be manhandled back to the station or taken in the car and who needed to be transported in the van.

They eased the van into the kerb beside a small throng of people surrounding a blustering senior constable and a babbling drunk. As they bundled the drunk into the back of the van, the senior constable gabbled abuse. The two young constables glanced at each other uneasily. It was fairly obvious that the senior constable, in uniform, was drunk himself. But he was their senior and there was little they could do but follow the usual procedure. Standing Orders prohibit three people riding in the front seat of the van and the routine was to take the offender back to the station, lodge him in the cells, and leave it to the arresting officer to follow on foot and complete the paper work. Reluctantly they drove off, leaving the senior constable still mumbling angrily to the bystanders.

They processed the drunk in the usual way: remove tie, belt and shoe laces, empty his pockets into a plastic bag and record the contents in the Property Book and, finally, lock him up. One of them muttered surprise as he wrote the figure '$250' in the right-hand column of the Property Book – an unusually large amount of cash to be carried by a drunk. The other shrugged and pushed the prisoner into the cell. They ambled outside to the van and resumed patrol.

Later they returned to the station to have a cup of coffee and to await knock-off time for the afternoon shift. One of them had a few things to tidy up in the watch-house. He happened to glance at his entry into the Property Book. It now read '$150'.

He whistled to his partner. They huddled in whispered conversation, checking and rechecking their memories of the earlier arrest.

Pete arrived at ten forty-five p.m., rostered for a night shift on the patrol car with young Mick, the newly graduated police cadet. He had barely slumped into a chair and lit a cigarette before two constables tapped on the partition which enclosed the sergeants' office. They were from the afternoon shift and, technically, not his responsibility but he was the only sergeant in the building and they seemed uneasy and twitchy. He listened to their story, interrupting now and then with questions about times, figures and locations. He followed them to the watch-house, glanced at the entry in the Property Book and told them to go home. He would, he assured them, check it out and let them know. Gratefully they left.

'Sarge, I've got all the gear in the car. When are we headed off?'

'Good on you, Mick. I wish to Christ I still had your enthusiasm. But look, mate, why don't you make yourself a cup of coffee. I've got a bit of paper work I want to check on first.'

Once the kid had disappeared to the mess room, Pete extracted the documents relating to the Drunk and Disorderly charge and sifted through them meticulously. The entry into the Property Book, examined under the harsh fluorescent light of the sergeants' room, was clearly a clumsy alteration. He double-checked the documents.

'What's wrong, Sarge?'

He started with embarrassment. Mick had returned to catch him hunched over the Property Book staring into space with resigned eyes, inch-long ash hanging precariously on the end of a dying cigarette.

'Nothing, mate. Let's get out on the road. We've got a particular job.'

During the drive to the senior constable's house he tersely outlined the situation to Mick.

Carl's wife answered the doorbell, blinking and sleepy. She told them what they already knew – that he was on the shift which finished at eleven – and, with some bitterness, she explained that he would probably be out on the town and unlikely to come home for some hours.

They checked all the late-licence pubs without success. Somewhere around two-thirty a.m. they tried the 'San Francisco Tavern'. Fred, the proprietor, shook his head but insisted that they come in anyway. The disco on the second floor closed at two a.m. and the crew of the station car often cruised by at that hour to shadow Fred as he took the evening's takings – several thousand dollars on a good night – down to the night safe of the bank. Fred appreciated the unobtrusive concern and often invited the crew in for a beer in the deserted bar while he fussed-about mopping floors, checking tills and switching off lights. Tonight, Pete gratefully accepted the invitation.

Fred was a gentle, balding camp. He noted the weariness ingrained into Pete's face and he ushered them into a side room, rather than into the deserted but brashly lit bar. He placed an opened bottle of beer and two glasses on the table and silently withdrew.

Young Mick had been there with Pete on several night shifts and knew the protocol. He, as driver, would drink nothing, his sergeant would finish the bottle, politely refuse more and both would thank the proprietor and return to the car. He relaxed and enjoyed the immobility. But tonight his older partner was frowning and restless.

'Sarge, it's late. I don't think we're going to find him. But even if we did, what are we supposed to do?'

Pete grunted and, with the reckless weariness of a week on night shift, he explained frankly: get the money back into the Property Cupboard before anyone noticed, tell the two divisional van constables to keep their mouths shut and obliquely inform Carl that it was time to apply for a transfer to another station.

They checked the house again. This time the lights were on. Carl opened the door, muttered incoherently and beckoned to them to follow him down the passageway.

A tiny electric radiator glowed ineffectually in the large, bare kitchen. The table was cluttered with dirty dishes, an overflowing ashtray and empty beer bottles. Carl placed two glasses on the table, unsteadily opened a bottle of beer and gestured towards some metal kitchen chairs. 'Boring night shift, eh? Know where you can find an old mate who'll always turn on a free beer, eh?' He giggled shrilly.

The two uniformed police remained standing.

'You stupid bastard!' Pete hissed. 'You know you're already skating on thin ice and now you risk your whole fucking career over a lousy hundred bucks ripped-off from some miserable drunk!'

'Aw, fuck off, Pete. I've poured you a beer . . . for chrissake sit down . . . that old bugger was so drunk he wouldn't know if the town hall tower was up him till the clock struck . . . he's not going to notice anything . . . anyway, what are you talking about . . . I don't know any drunk . . . what drunk . . . are you accusing me?'

Pete remained motionless. 'Carl, shut up. The kids on the divie van noticed the Property Book. Now give us back the missing money quick!'

'Money, money, money!' Carl cackled, pulling a fistful of crumpled notes from his shirt pocket and showering them over the empty bottles on the table.

'A hundred bucks, Carl, a hundred bucks.'

Carl squinted at Pete and his shoulders bunched like a ferret. 'So, so, so! So the snotty little sergeant is cross because he didn't get his cut, eh? Didn't get his cut . . . tut, tut . . . tuttety-tut!'

'Cut, tut, tuttety-tut!' he gabbled, scooping up handfuls of notes and throwing them at the standing figures. Pete turned and Mick followed, leaving the money scattered on the floor.

The station was silent at five a.m. Mick made two cups of coffee in the empty mess room. 'What now, Sarge?'

'I don't know. The drunk will be awake soon. I've got about forty bucks on me, what have you got?'

Without speaking, Mick extracted his wallet and held it upside-down apologetically.

'Mick, go down to the watch-house. Bill should be on duty. Ask him if he can lend me sixty bucks until the banks open.'

Mick returned in a few minutes. 'I didn't talk to Bill: I checked the Watch-house Book first. The drunk was bailed out by his wife an hour ago.'

Pete sat in silence, mechanically lighting a cigarette. He gazed at the wall for some minutes and eventually murmured: 'Mick, would you go down to the radio and put in a request for the night shift duty officer to attend the station?'

*   *   *   *

Officially the shift ended at seven a.m. In fact it was near enough to eleven before the two could change into civilian clothes and stumble out into the sunshine.

The duty officer had talked with Pete for half-an-hour and phoned the superintendent; he had arrived at daybreak, discussed it with them, checked the station books and phoned the chief superintendent. By nine a.m., all of them, including Carl, had been assembled in the sergeants' office. Carl had been handed a typed letter of resignation for signature and then formally charged with theft.

They walked the two blocks to the 'San Francisco Tavern'. Fred, freshly shaven and pink-cheeked, glanced at the two and nodded towards the side room. Again, he placed a bottle of beer and two glasses on the table and left them alone.

Mick's eyes were red-rimmed with tiredness and he scratched at the patchy, adolescent stubble around his chin. He wanted to comfort Pete but had no words or gestures. After the second beer he tried awkwardly to break the silence.

'I'm sorry, Sarge.'

'Why? What did you do?'

'No, no, I mean I'm sorry it worked out like that. The blokes say that you and Carl went through Recruits together. It must be ... well ... sort of hard for you. I mean, I realise that you and I will have to go into the witness box for the Prosecution when the theft business comes to court.'

Pete stared into his beer. 'I've spent a lot of time in the witness box', he said. 'No, mate, it's not that. Mick, you just watched the death of a copper. He's in his thirties ... fifteen years service and nothing to show for it but a fucked-up marriage and a drinking problem. He's out of The Job now and who wants him? Even that miserable old stand-by – work as a security guard or nightwatchman – is out when you've got a conviction for theft. It chops out most government jobs and he's not fit enough to hold down a labouring job. He'll be a dribbling derelict in five years and dead in seven.'

Mick nodded silently. Unable to think of anything appropriate to say, he poured another beer.

EXHIBIT A

His Honour, my boss, was due for his biennial leave from Papua New Guinea. He departed to watch the test cricket series at Lords while staying at his London club. He would be replaced by a locum tenens – a younger District Court judge from Australia who was being groomed for elevation to the Supreme Court bench – and the monthly circuits would continue as usual.

In the absence of the judge, I organised the routine end-of-month 'call over': the conference between prosecution and defence barristers and the judge or his associate to agree upon which cases would go to court in that circuit, the order in which they would be heard, and the travel arrangements needed.

The Public Solicitor's Office sent along Nick, the amiable young barrister with the squinty eye and the impish grin who had been with us on many circuits. He would act as Defence Counsel for all of the accused.

Crown Law Department sent Callaghan, the abrasive young man-about-town of Port Moresby, who would act as Prosecutor.

Callaghan thumped a thick file on my desk. 'You're not going to believe this,' he smirked, 'but we've got a bestiality case!'

He flipped the file open and extracted the indictment: the formal statement of accusation, typed on soft-green bond paper embossed with the seal of the Supreme Court. We all knew that I, as associate, would eventually have to read the indictment aloud in the courtroom and he composed his face into mock solemnity and mimicked my drawl:

'Husat Istap, you stand charged that on or about the sixteenth day of October one thousand nine hundred and seventy one at the village of Buai in the Territory of Papua New Guinea you did have carnal knowledge of one canine bitch contrary to

Section 625(a) of the Criminal Code. How do you plead: guilty or not guilty?'

Nick chuckled and rose to his feet as if addressing the court. 'And you will note, Your Honour, that it was a *female* dog: there is nothing strange about *my* client!'

I riffled through the documents in disbelief as Callaghan outlined the circumstances of the alleged offence.

Apparently the accused was an elderly villager from some obscure hamlet on the banks of the Fly River. He had only one wife who happened to be pregnant and unable to share in intercourse at the time and he had stomped off into the jungle garden with his dog in anger and frustration. It seems that he owned a coconut tree which he was tapping for *tuba*. The growing shoots of the coconut palm are skilfully incised, much like a rubber tree, and the sap oozes into a bamboo cylinder where it ferments. Tuba was the only form of alcohol known in Papua New Guinea before the intrusion of the White Man. It is thick, white and tasty, but dangerously unpredictable: the alcohol content varying erratically according to the age of the tree, the ephemeral climatic conditions and the time it is left to ferment. Apparently this particular tree was 'over proof' and he had drunk himself into a semi-stupor. In the drowsy late-afternoon sunshine he had done something indelicate with his dog. A neighbour had stumbled upon them in the garden. The neighbour was an 'enemy' within the context of those petty inter-family feuds which animate life in a tiny village and supply the gossip which is the major form of recreation. The neighbour had reported the matter to the local patrol post.

We searched the documents in the file for some clue as to how the incident had culminated in a case before the Supreme Court. Under normal circumstances the patrol officer in charge of the patrol post would – if he had any maturity and sensitivity – have offered some anti-hangover aspirin and gently but firmly informed the old man that such practices tend to give the sub-district a bad name and would he kindly perform them in someone else's sub-district the next time. We could only guess that the patrol officer was under the eyes of some visiting official from

Port Moresby and had felt obliged to follow the procedures laid down by the Papua New Guinea Criminal Code. The Code provides a maximum sentence of fifteen years' imprisonment with hard labour for 'the abominable crime of buggery'.

A Crown Prosecutor's file is a jumble of police records of interview, statements from witnesses, transcripts of evidence given to the lower court, assorted legal documents and administrative memoranda. As we pieced it together, the story unfolded further.

The District Headquarters on the island of Daru had been informed, on one of the twice-daily radio transmissions from the remote patrol post, that a villager had been charged with an indictable offence. The only access to that area is via the swirling, muddy waters of the Fly River and Headquarters had reluctantly organised a patrol of six members of the Royal Papua New Guinea Constabulary, under the command of a Corporal, to bring the prisoner into custody. They were equipped with an aluminium dinghy with outboard motor and carried rations, fresh water, and their .303 rifles with six rounds of ammunition per man. It took them three days, against the current, to reach the hamlet. There, the headman greeted them. He had, he announced, been informed that one of his people had committed an offence against The Law; thus, he had, some days earlier, despatched the person and his dog by canoe to report to the District Headquarters at Daru and accept the discipline of the White Man's court.

The headman proudly wore the battered army cap with its brass badge which the Department of District Administration issues to a *Luluai*: a senior resident of a hamlet appointed by the visiting patrol officer as responsible for government affairs. Had they not, he enquired, noticed anyone waving to them as canoes passed in opposite directions on the bustling river? His was a civilised village and he was sure that one of his people would have respectfully saluted a passing police patrol.

The patrol slept that night in the village and then set off down-river. They reached Daru two-and-a-half days later to find that the gentleman had dutifully presented himself to District

Headquarters and had been committed for trial and lodged in the cells along with his dog.

The documents did not indicate whether separate cells were provided. A terse hand-written comment in the margin of one of the memoranda did suggest that the Corporal in charge of the patrol had, on return, been a little irritated by the sleek appearance of the accused and his dog, both of whom would have enjoyed a week living on police rations whose protein content contrasts sharply with the soggy sago which is the staple diet of the impoverished villagers of the Upper Fly. The Corporal's grumpy marginal note also suggested that headquarters rations are sumptuous in comparison with those issued to a motor boat patrol.

A Crown Prosecutor has a certain degree of discretion in that he can indicate that he intends to lead no evidence at the trial and can thus effectively abort it. I drew Callaghan's attention to the enormous cost to the tax-payer of sending – on behalf of one deflowered dog – a judge, his associate, a prosecution barrister and a defence barrister to the island of Daru in a chartered twin-engined aircraft. (Regulations require that twin-engined aeroplanes be used as they have a slightly lower probability of crashing through engine failure and, although associates and barristers are expendable, Supreme Court judges are expensive items to replace.)

Callaghan pointed out that we had another case – a multiple murder – which would have to be heard at Daru anyway and so my grumblings were irrelevant. We agreed upon a date of departure.

*   *   *   *

I attended the Port Moresby airport to meet the new judge and explain that I would be his aide-de-camp for the next two months.

He strode through the customs barrier and shook my hand warmly.

It was difficult to resist instinctively liking him. He was a tall, gangly Australian with a broad open face and was obviously excited by the prospect of spending two months in a demanding job in a strange country.

'The letter from the Attorney-General,' he said, 'hinted that we would be spending much of our time out on circuit. Whereabouts?'

'Western Papua for the first month, Sir. It will involve a fair bit of travelling in the back-blocks.'

'Sounds interesting!' he said and I winced. He was clearly unaware that the seven judges of the Supreme Court maintained, like any other group of workers, a pecking order of privilege and he, as the junior newcomer, had been assigned to the circuit which the other judges loathed. 'Western Papua' meant four weeks of constant travel, living out of a suitcase and sleeping in cockroach-infested bungalows attached to the patrol posts of poverty-stricken Sub-Districts.

'What sort of cases will I be dealing with?'

'Just the usual stuff, Sir: mainly wilful murders with a couple of manslaughters, plus one or two . . . er . . . odd ones.'

'Great!' he said and I ushered him to the chauffeur-driven car waiting outside the airport terminal.

*   *   *   *

The last leg of the flight to Daru is always depressing. The Colgate-white pattern of coral reefs sprawled below blue water begins to blur as one approaches the centre of the Gulf of Papua: silt from the rivers flowing into the Gulf muddies the water and mangrove swamps replace the white beaches. The island of Daru itself is a desolate protrusion of mud and jungle.

The District Commissioner and a senior police officer met us and we were escorted to the courthouse.

It is a superb building: the weight-bearing beams are of European-style squared timber, with metal bolts, but the roof and walls are of woven thatch, and the soaring gables follow the lines of the traditional New Guinea *haus tambarin* – the spiritual centre of most of the larger coastal villages. The new judge was awed by the architecture and asked eager questions as I showed him to the small room attached to the back of the building.

Outside, a squad of the Royal Papua New Guinea Constabulary, in parade ground formation, stood restlessly in the 'at ease' position. A warrant officer paced up and down the two lines of men. Their blue berets were sloped correctly, the light-blue shirts were creased immaculately and the gaiters and boots glistened with spit polish. Brass belt buckles winked in the mid-morning sunshine. Each held a Lee-Enfield rifle with fixed bayonet.

The judge peered through the small louvred window. 'My god, what happens now?'

I explained that it was traditional for the Supreme Court judge conducting the first sitting of the year in the District to be greeted by a guard of honour. They would salute him with a 'present arms' and the Guard Commander would invite him to inspect the guard.

He grinned. 'Christ, I never got beyond the rank of corporal in World War II and I've been through this nonsense before. But it might be fun to play the part of the inspecting officer. What do I have to do?'

I outlined the procedure usually adopted by my boss: accept the salute of the guard commander with dignity, remain at attention while they 'present arms' and the bugler completes his salute and then move slowly down the two lines of men, commenting occasionally on their bearing. If possible, one should make a note of which man has the largest collection of medals on his chest, pause before him, enquire how long he has been in the Service, mutter something like: 'Well, done, Corporal!' and move on.

I am sure he chuckled quietly as I helped him into his scarlet robes, attached the black sash around his waist and adjusted the wig.

I discreetly remained in the rear room and lit a cigarette. I had a mass of paperwork to get through before the court sat and was barely conscious of the ringing tones of the bugle and the rippling thump of fifteen rifle butts hitting the ground as the Guard Commander bellowed: 'Order arms!'

The judge returned to the room with a bemused grin. 'Christ,' he muttered, 'they're a fine body of men. Fit, disciplined and dignified. The Commander would have put my old army drill sergeant to shame with the way he snaps to attention. And the bugler . . . what was the call he gave?'

I explained that it was the Royal Salute. Legal tradition maintains the myth that a Supreme Court judge visits the colonial District as an envoy of that London lady who fancies corgies.

He nodded.

'Speaking of dogs,' he added, 'why was there a constable standing alone near the courtroom door holding a dog on a leash?'

'Er . . . *that*, Sir, is "Exhibit A" in your first case.'

26

ANOTHER BARBEQUE

On completion of the six p.m. to two a.m. shift on a Saturday night they generally gathered for a barbeque. At two o'clock in the morning it was hardly comfortable – steaks charred in the darkness and the temperature of the chilled cans of beer was often little different from that of the wind of Melbourne nights – but it was a happy ritual. For most of them Saturday signalled the end of the weekly shift. They could relax, swap gossip and not bother to count the number of cans of beer consumed, anticipating the luxury of a Sunday morning sleep-in and a couple of weeks of undemanding day shift.

There was a public picnic area down by the river bank, complete with barbeque plate, and the crew of the divisional van would always check it out on their last run through the neighbourhood at about one forty-five a.m. They had a cryptic radio message which indicated to the rest of the station staff, CIB and uniformed, that the picnic area was deserted and they could load up the beers and steaks and assemble.

In September, Ferret was on the van with Louie-the-Lip, his older partner. They drove down the bumpy track to the riverside and halted at the edge of the picnic area. There was a sedan parked squarely beside the barbeque.

'Damn!' Louie muttered, 'Go and check it out, mate.'

Ferret returned to the seat of the van after a couple of minutes. 'It's a bloke and his bird. They look OK – ordinary sort of people – but he's chock a block up her.'

'Dinky di? Christ, but it's a small sedan. Missionary position?'

'God knows what you call *that* position! They're in the front seat – steering wheel, gear shift lever and Christ knows what else – don't know how he manages.'

'Half his luck.'

'Yeah but what about the barbeque? They're really into it – having a ball – they didn't even notice me walking over there. He must be getting close to the vinegar stroke and he's not going to take kindly to the suggestion that he clears out and leaves the barbeque area for our blokes.'

'Aw, there's always some way of handling these situations', Louie grunted, opening the van door. 'Come on.'

They walked across the picnic area, Ferret following the circle of light from his partner's torch.

Louie tapped gently on the window of the car. There was a flurry of tangled limbs, whispered exclamations and hasty rearrangement of underwear. The window wound down cautiously.

'I'm sorry to disturb you, Sir,' said Louie, 'but have you seen him?'

'Seen *who*?' stammered the pale face framed by the car's window.

'The bloke with the axe.'

'*What* bloke with an axe? You're not serious are you?'

'Sir,' said Ferret, leaning over Louie's shoulder, 'you don't think we'd be patrolling this area at two o'clock in the morning if it wasn't an emergency, do you?'

'Jesus no! Thanks for warning me. I'll let you know if I see him.'

He fumbled between simultaneous attempts to rezip his fly and get the key into the ignition switch. The engine whined with a slipping clutch as the car accelerated up the muddy track from the river bank.

They walked back to the van.

Ferret picked up the microphone. At the station, the constable manning the radio received the signal and nodded towards the others. They began unpacking chops and steak from the mess room fridge and putting crushed ice around the beer cans.

27

MEMBER DOWN

She had cooked his favourite dish: steak and kidney pie, done in her way with a trace of garlic. It was a tradition – unmentioned but woven into their lives – that she cooked something a bit special for their first meal together when he returned to the sane hours of day shift. Sandra was a school teacher and was normally home by about four p.m.: they could at least share an evening meal when he was on the eleven p.m. night shift. But the week-long afternoon shifts – three to eleven p.m. – were desolate gaps.

She chatted about the staff politics of the school. Although comparatively young, there was a good chance that she would get the deputy principal's job next year.

He ate and listened. Listened not so much to the words as to her presence. Years ago, when they met once a week for a meal in that restaurant in Carlton, he would find himself losing the thread of what she was saying as he watched: watched her gentle firmness, the femininity of that hair brushing her shoulders as she spoke, and the quiet determination.

Yet, paradoxically, it was the strength of her self-control which sometimes worried him these days. I suppose, he thought, the feeling ultimately goes back to the business of having kids. The final diagnosis of the doctors – that it was medically impossible for them to conceive children together – had hurt him deeply, in a way which he could not articulate to her. He knew that she was just as deeply hurt but she handled it with characteristic determination, sublimating her disappointment by working with even more commitment to the primary school children whom she taught. To him, that was logical but resolved nothing. He was conscious of a troubled vacuum somewhere inside.

'Dave, are you listening to me or are you off again moping about The Job?'

He grinned sadly, muttered an apology and asked questions about the doings of the school staff. She launched into a description of problems with the new trainee teachers.

He had tried to share her friends but, in the end, he reflected, had been unsuccessful. Part of the trouble was the damned house. Their plans of finding an old home in the inner suburbs had crumbled on contact with the reality of land values – grossly inflated by the movement of young trendies into the old working-class areas – and they had ended up buying a near-new brick veneer place on a housing estate near Croydon, some twenty or thirty kilometres from the city. It was modern, hygienic and spacious but a long way from Sandra's work. Visits from friends tended to be formal, pre-arranged evenings, rather than the spontaneity of borrowing a spanner or dropping in for a beer when the fridge ran dry on a puritanical Melbourne Sunday. Shift work made it no easier, and his contacts with Sandra's colleagues were distorted by the stilted settings in which they met. The house itself was fine – airy and comfortable if a little pretentious – but the neighbourhood was impersonal. Ironically, a large number of houses on the estate were occupied by police members: the last people he wanted to yarn with in off-duty hours.

He realised that she had fallen silent. He rose to his feet. 'That was beaut. I'll make the coffee.'

Through the serving hatch to the kitchen, he said: 'And how long will you have these trainee teachers with you?'

'Dave, I just explained all that.'

He returned with two cups of coffee. 'I'm sorry, Sandy. I suppose I wasn't really listening.'

'That's OK, I suppose there wasn't really much to listen to. There's not much left, is there, that we can share?'

'Oh, come on! You make it sound like our marriage is falling apart around the seams.'

She checked the impulse to say: 'Is it?' Instead, she asked about his work at the station. She did the washing up and went to bed alone. He opened a bottle of scotch.

*   *   *   *

The next morning he studied the station roster. A long weekend was coming up. He nagged the Senior Sergeant until they had reorganised it to give him four consecutive days off, which would coincide with Sandra's weekend if she took a 'sickie' from school on the Friday. It meant swapping shifts with another sergeant who complained bitterly but eventually gave in to Dave's pleas.

He came home and suggested to Sandra that they get away from the city for a few days. He said it like a child shyly offering a birthday present. She responded like a child receiving one: it was unexpected and exciting. They spent the evening discussing possibilities. The final decision was hers: they would rent an on-site caravan at the park at Narbethong on the Black Spur. It was a crazy idea and typical of Sandra. Narbethong, seventy of eighty kilometres from Melbourne, has nothing but expanses of rugged mountain bush, a nice old pub and a caravan park. They had stopped at the pub for a counter lunch years before and she had been enchanted by the bush parrots which fed from her hand on the verandah.

'And we won't even take a radio with us', she kissed him gently. 'If World War Three breaks out, some other bastard can worry about it.'

*   *   *   *

Arriving at work the next morning, he routinely checked the sheaf of telex messages. One of them cancelled all police leave in 'Q' District for the coming Sunday. The Prime Minister was to officially open a nursing home in Fitzroy and a political demonstration was expected. Independent Patrol Group would handle it, with the Mounted Branch in reserve and back-up from all district stations.

He made no attempt to break it gently to her that evening: he simply described the telex message. In the old days she would have sobbed with disappointment and held him tightly. But those days were gone. She did indeed break into tears but, as he had anticipated, it was bitter, angry crying and she turned all her frustration on to him, snapping accusations to which there was no reply. Again she went to bed alone; again Dave opened a bottle of scotch.

On the Wednesday morning he received the fifteen-page Operation Order detailing plans for control of the demonstration. He read it in cold fury. Elections for Federal Parliament were due in three weeks and the Prime Minister was campaigning for re-election on a cynical platform of fear: 'The world is going to pieces! Your only hope of survival is blind trust in the ruling classes!' Law and order was a major issue. A piddling little nursing home did not need a Prime Minister to declare it open and Dave had no doubts about the political motivation involved. Fitzroy was a solid labor seat, a mixture of militant working-class unionists and naive, middle-class trendies; hordes of disorganised lefties would show up to express their frustration, blood would be spilt, the television cameras would whirr and the Prime Minister would score several thousand votes from timid little people appalled by the spectacle. As usual, the police would be the meat in the sandwich.

Sullenly, he attended the briefing at Divisional Headquarters on the Saturday. He was to be a sector sergeant responsible for a group of twelve constables from the Preston and Northcote Sub-districts who would be held in reserve and have the additional role of providing perimeter security around the brawler van which would be parked about two-hundred-and-fifty metres down from the nursing home. 'The brawler' was the big clumsy van used to hold offenders when there were too many to transport in divisional vans. If, as anticipated, Independent Patrol Group made a number of arrests, there could be attempts by the crowd to hinder offenders being bundled into the van; Dave's section was to provide a protective cordon around it.

He underlined the relevant sections of the Operation Order in the clipboard on his knee as the briefing officer elaborated on it

171

in a nasal monotone. Basically it was a routine operation. Dave's section would be equipped with one portable radio tuned to the Command Post channel; his men would report to the location at 1300 hours; as usual, no firearms would be carried – though Special Operations Group would be on stand-by at their base – and batons would be produced only on the explicit order of an officer of the rank of chief inspector or above; all questions from the media would be referred to the media liaison officer, who would be situated at the intersection of ... the briefing officer droned on and Dave lost interest. In any case, it was all contained in the operation order on his knee. Its fifteen pages covered all contingencies.

*   *   *   *

By one-fifteen it was hot, unusually hot for Melbourne in Spring. Leaves on the trees in the adjoining park hung sullen and limp. A crowd of a thousand to fifteen-hundred dawdled noisily around the entrance to the nursing home waiting for the arrival of the Prime Minister and his entourage. Placards poked above the throng but Dave, two-hundred-and-fifty metres down the side street, could not read them.

He briefed his section of twelve constables for the second time and explained the arrangements for the mobile canteen. It could turn into a long boring afternoon, he warned, and so he would dispatch them in rotating pairs every sixty minutes to take a ten-minute tea break at the canteen caravan.

There was nothing more to say or do and the group settled into a loose circle around the brawler van, lighting cigarettes, edging into the shade offered by one side of the tall van, and chatting quietly.

Punctually at two p.m. the Prime Minister arrived and entered the building. They could hear the ragged tumult of shouting and see confused movement but, at that distance, it was impossible to assess what was going on. Nervous wisecracks rippled around the group of young constables. 'The trendies are getting their kicks!' 'Much more fun that pottery or group-fucking!' Dave stood impassively, squinting in an attempt to follow the tangled movement in the distance. Things were being thrown – eggs and fruit only, he hoped. Three Independent Patrol Group (IPG) members moved towards them dragging a student. Half-a-dozen demonstrators followed, heckling the IPG men, but abandoned the pursuit after forty or fifty metres and returned to the excitement of the crowd frothing around the entrance to the building. In Dave's sector there were only a few civilians timidly watching at a distance and there was nothing for him to do but stand back and allow the IPG constables to firmly bundle the student into the van through the rear doors.

Relative stillness settled. He despatched two constables for a break at the mobile canteen. At two-thirty there was momentary movement as two uniformed men hauled a heckler out of the hall and carried him down to the van. He was feigning unconsciousness but abandoned the pretence when he realised that the crowd had not followed and that he was a long way from the television news cameras. He meekly clambered into the back of the van and the double doors swung shut. Dave lit a cigarette and despatched another two constables for a tea break.

There was an odd, restless movement in the crowd. He tensed and ground out the cigarette on the pavement. He squinted into the bright afternoon sunshine but could discern only that the crowd around the entrance appeared to be oozing in his direction. The noise increased. He muttered a warning to the man beside him.

Then there was a surging movement down the side street. Shouting. Feet clattering on the pavement in gathering momentum. A hundred metres form the brawler van an inspector, patently as puzzled as Dave as to what was happening, shouted orders to some constables to form a line and block the movement of the crowd. In the narrow street it was like a wave breaking on rocks: thundering movement breaking into eddies and then ebbing and rolling into the next surge. The portable radio, held by a senior constable at Dave's shoulder, crackled. The field commander was moving up three reserve sections of IPG to support the line. They jog-trotted up from behind Dave's group to form a line of blue across the street.

Snatches of shouting made it clear what had happened: a rumour had swept the crowd that the Prime Minister was leaving by a rear entrance which opened onto the side street. Dave mentally rechecked the Operation Order and confirmed that the rumour was false, but that hardly mattered now: the crowd was bottled into the street in bitter confrontation with the line of police which was being pushed slowly towards him.

Stones and fruit were being thrown and the noise was a low confused roar overlaid by a staccato crackle of shouts. 'Fascist pigs!' 'Get off my foot!' 'Copper cunts!' 'For chrissake somebody help me!' 'Pigs!' Dave's mind flashed a momentary memory of a winter's morning he had spent watching waves batter the rocks at Phillip Island: the deep surging roar and, over it, the hiss and splatter of foam. He glanced anxiously at his men. The lanky trainee constable from Northcote was pale with fear and the rest fidgeted uneasily. By now the firm blue line blocking the street had dissolved into a ragged half-circle with a no-man's land of about twenty metres enclosing the smaller circle of Dave's men clustered anxiously around the brawler van.

The half-circle held and the noise lulled a little. But individual scuffles continued. Every few minutes a couple of police members would emerge dragging a civilian who would be thrown into the van. Dave felt anxious and useless.

He swore softly as he watched an obese, over-confident, young IPG constable lunge out of the throng dragging a skinny civilian by the beard. 'The bloody idiot!' Dave muttered to no-one but himself, 'He's been trained in how to restrain an assailant with an arm lock; this sort of macho tactic is going to end up with him getting kicked in the balls or else in enraging the crowd.'

His mumbled observation underestimated the situation. The crowd was galvanised by the spectacle of the frightened demonstrator stumbling in pathetic indignity as the fat constable jerked at his beard. The shouts escalated into hysterical abuse and the crowd swirled. A slim teenage girl in jeans threw herself at a six-foot constable, shrieking and clawing in futile hatred.

Dave's eyes swept around the circle of his men. They were scared and bewildered. Again, he swore savagely as he noted that the Mounted Branch was assembling behind them, the horses snorting and stamping nervously. Dave winced. 'Christ almighty, the horses are a savagely efficient way of breaking up a mob but, in this narrow street, the last thing we need is the panic they will create!'

A constable and senior constable lurched towards the van dragging a squirming kid of about nineteen who kicked wildly and shouted incoherent obscenities. 'Let him go, you copper cunts!' someone screamed and a tangled mass of demonstrators fell upon the three of them, clawing and clutching at arms and legs. The mass swayed backwards and forwards, a flurry of limbs, grimacing faces and the kid shouting: 'For chrissake lay off! You're tearing me apart!'

With a sweep of his arm, Dave stopped a constable on his left from instinctively plunging into the fray: their job was to hold the perimeter around the van, not to assist with arrests. In any case, the no-man's land was gone and there was a swirl of angry people between them and the police struggling with the kid.

The senior constable holding the kid in a headlock kicked savagely at one of the would-be rescuers and hauled him free from the tangle; he glanced anxiously towards the circle of police around the van, saw that there was no hope of forcing his way through the crowd, and threw the kid against the cast-iron fence of a house and snapped a handcuff around one wrist and the other around the elegant Victorian iron upright of the fence. The kid sank to his knees, one handcuffed arm stretched awkwardly above his head while the senior constable merged back into the chaos.

Another civilian was thrown into the back of the van, legs flailing. Dave and two constables heaved their shoulders against the double doors, trying to close them against his kicking. Demonstrators swarmed over them, pulling at the doors and clawing at the police. 'Let him go, you pigs! He hasn't done anything wrong!' The doors swayed back and forth in an eerie dance.

Dave became conscious of a steady chant booming through the surf. 'Wait till we get the guns! Wait till we get the guns!' His racing mind at first registered puzzlement – what do they mean? No police member present is carrying firearms – and then bitter, bewildered anger. It was a mindless, alien chant – alien to the Australia that Dave knew – and threatening. But he had no time to get his thoughts together. His eyes swept over what was left of the circle of his men. It had now dissolved into a boiling confusion of unconnected skirmishes.

But there did seem to be a focus to the movement – the eye of the cyclone – which revolved around a mass of young people encircling the kid handcuffed to the fence. It was there that the chanting centred. A girl in jeans and ragged shirt was holding a megaphone and shouting: 'Police riot! Police riot'!

Dave swung around to the police member beside him – a young detective in plain clothes whom he did not know by name. 'For chrissake,' he snapped to him, 'get that kid off the fence and into the van – he's forming a focal point for the crowd.'

The detective, sweating heavily, hesitated – unused to being given a shouted command by an unknown uniformed sergeant – and then nodded understanding. 'Back him up!' Dave bellowed at three constables from Preston, who plunged into the crowd, following his pointed direction. Dave remained with the remnants of the circle around the van and watched as the four fought their way through to the kid. The young detective crouched over the spitting kid, fumbling with the handcuff keys. He shouted something at one of the Preston constables, who handed over his set of keys. Swearing evenly, the ashen-faced plain-clothesman tried again to unlock the handcuffs, his hands trembling uncontrollably. Dave, catching glimpses of this through the shifting melee, also swore. 'Oh Christ! The kid has been grabbed by someone from IPG with the new-issue handcuffs and no-one has the new-style keys to fit them. Shit!'

He slapped a shrieking teenage girl away from him and tried to elbow his way towards them. As he moved he caught a glimpse of a young bearded man, eyes blank with hatred, lurching against him. It was momentary. Dave's consciousness exploded into blinding flashes of light as hard metal slammed across his cheek bone and temple.

He stumbled forward, ending in a half-kneeling position at the demonstrator's feet. Instinctively he swung his right arm up and around to protect his head and his left arm down to protect his groin from kicking. He glimpsed a familiar face: it was Moose, the young constable from Preston, looming up through the tangled mass and shouting something incomprehensible. Moose snapped his left arm around the demonstrator's neck from behind in a rough head lock which jerked him backwards; simultaneously Moose slipped the baton from his right-hand pocket and stabbed savagely – short, hard lunges with the point of the baton, going expertly for the kidneys. The demonstrator screamed in agony, dropped the length of pipe he was clutching and his knees buckled under him. Moose slid the baton back into his pocket and released the head lock. The demonstrator sagged to his knees and then toppled face down amid the trampling feet.

'Sarge! Sarge! Are you all right?'

Still half-kneeling, Dave wavered one hand across his face. He could detect no sensation other than the wetness of the blood gushing between his fingers. 'Yes, of course I'm all right! But Moose, that kid you went for . . . for chrissake get him to an ambulance . . . the kidneys! And Moose, the baton . . . for chrissake don't admit anything to any officer . . . and . . . and. . .'

He lost consciousness, toppling forwards on his face beside the demonstrator.

The crowd swirled around the two bloodied figures lying parallel on the pavement.

EPILOGUE:
TRIBUTE TO A DEAD MATE

We had been expecting it for several decades but, on 4 August 1994, Bill Collins finally carked it. As I write, his wake is still in progress and will continue for many months in some of the pubs of inner Melbourne. I no longer attend funerals and certainly cannot afford to buy wreathes or bunches of flowers and so the only tribute I can offer is to add to this book one last, brief anecdote.

He was an ebullient yarn-teller: a shanakee who would never allow mundane facts to interfere with a living story. I still chuckle over his recounting of his brief employment with the Royal Melbourne Institute of Technology.

Bill was as ugly as sin. Underneath the leathery skin and straggly beard, he had a craggy bone structure. It was as if a sculptor had selected a lump of granite, chipped out angular chunks and then abandoned the project, despairing of ever developing it into the smoothness of a Rodin bust. His main stamping ground was the pubs of Carlton in the days before that suburb became gentrified. I never knew of him holding a permanent job but then Bill was unclassifiable. He drifted convivially among circles of the radical students of Melbourne University or the Institute of Technology, the crims of Carlton, the drunks of the 'Albion' pub and the pseudo-intellectuals of 'Watson's' wine bar.

The students loved him and one day a very nubile young art student from the Institute of Technology gushed about his sculptured features and begged him to pose and let her do a conté sketch of his face. Bill's libidinal drive never faltered throughout his sixty or seventy years of existence and he agreed, anticipating carnal reward. In fact the very attractive girl returned a week later to say that her tutor had raved about the sketch. The tutor, she explained, had been ecstatic about the 'real' challenges of life drawing and had asked her to invite Bill to consider accepting part-time work as a model for the evening life-drawing sessions.

He was a little bemused. The label 'artists' model' hardly fitted with the many epithets which had been applied to him but he was, as usual, short of money and agreed. It worked out well: he simply had to sit still for an hour or so and, after each session, he was paid in cash and could happily drink with the students in the nearby pub.

Strolling down Lygon Street a month later he instinctively noted the unmarked car from Carlton CIB parked in the kerb ahead of him. Two detectives emerged and he winced. There had been a number of unpleasant interchanges with these two gentlemen over the years. It had begun when they had blustered into the back room of an espresso bar and demanded to know what he was doing there. With instinctive response to their aggressiveness Bill had announced that he was the Ecumenical Adviser to the Archbishop of Canterbury on a mission to enhance Anglo/Italian relations and they had beat the hell out of him for giving sarcastic lip. This time he feigned unawareness of them but they blocked the footpath.

'OK, Bill. Into the car and we'll have a little chat down at the station.'

He walked fatalistically into the CIB interview room which was not exactly unfamiliar to him. Bill had no serious criminal record: his 'crime' was that he was known to police. They could not put a label to him but were aware that he mingled easily with many of the crims of Carlton. Legally he was clean. There may have been the occasional dodgy deal with some of his friends but that was not on the record. There was merely the matter of several incidents when the police, with ungentlemanly zeal, had charged him with 'Drunk and Disorderly' after pleasant evenings of celebration with colleagues.

The two detectives settled themselves into chairs, leaving Bill standing in front of the desk.

'OK, Bill. What are you up to these days?'

'Nothing. I'm as clean as a whistle.'

'Yeah, yeah, yeah. Bill, by now you should know that we don't like getting fucked around with evasive answers. As we hear it on the grape vine you've actually been buying people beers in the pubs instead of cadging off them. So what's the go? Dealing in a bit of stolen property or knocking off the odd credit card, are we?'

'No. Dead set! I'm straight.'

'So where's the money coming from?'

'Well, I've got a bit of regular casual work at the Royal Melbourne Institute of Technology.'

'Go on! So RMIT is short of a Professor of Space Engineering, is it? Don't give us shit, Bill. What sort of job?'

Bill paused. He knew these two plods: if he were to say 'artists' model', they would fall apart with laughter and then belt the shit out of him for giving smart-arse answers.

'Well, er, it's in the Maintenance Department – you know, emptying garbage cans, mowing lawns and that sort of thing.'

There was a thoughtful silence and then the senior detective lifted the telephone and dialled a number. After several minutes of muttered conversation he put the phone down and rose to his feet. 'The Maintenance Section of RMIT says that they have never heard of you.' he said before swinging a savage right cross to Bill's chest. The other detective put in a swing to the left ear and Bill crumpled to the floor.

They sat stolidly in their chairs until he eventually got to his feet.

'So you're getting money from some mythical job at RMIT, are you?'

'No. This is all a misunderstanding. I do work there. It's just that . . . well, Maintenance Section mightn't have me on their books because most of my time is spent with Buildings Section – you know, cleaning toilets and that sort of thing.'

The two detectives exchanged glances silently and eventually one reached for the phone. On completion of the conversation he stood up, replacing the phone on its cradle as he leaned towards Bill with a swinging backhander across the face.

As Bill was spun around by its force, the other detective kneed him expertly in the groin.

Face down on the floor, Bill pondered. He had been through many punch-ups but was now getting old and could not take it as easily. Instinctively he checked the feelings from his rib cage for possible fracture. With resignation he rolled and painfully got himself over onto his hands and knees.

'All right, you bastards, I can't take any more. I'll tell you the truth. I do work at RMIT. I am an artists' model.'

Roaring with laughter, they put in a last few punches as they dragged him to the door and bundled him out on to the street.

'Collins never gives up, does he?' said the senior detective to his partner, wiping blood from his knuckles with a handkerchief.

What they never understood was the irony. Bill never *did* give up. To the day of his death he would still retell, with glee, his account of a small but rather glorious misunderstanding.

Rest in peace, Bill Collins.

UNIVERSITIES AT MEDWAY LIBRARY